PRESENTS

WRITTEN BY KEVIN REYNOLDS
BASED ON THE SCREENPLAY BY DAVID KOEP & MICHAEL CRICHTON
AND THE NOVEL BY MICHAEL CRICHTON

First published in 1997 by Screenscene Ltd., Leeds, England.

Screenscene Ltd., Rose Wharf, East Street, Leeds LS9 8EE.

ISBN: 1 901794 00 8

Layout and Design: David Whitworth.

Written and Edited by: Kevin Reynolds.

Reprographics by Creative Convergence, Leeds.

Printed and bound in the UK by Speedprint (Horsforth) Ltd., Leeds.

JURASSIC PARK

THE LOST WORLD
JURASSIC PARK

THE COMPLETE STORY

Dr. Alan Grant

Sam Neill

Dr. Ellie Slater

Laura Dern

Dr. John Hammond

Lord Richard Attenborough

Dr. Ian Malcolm

Jeff Goldblum

Alexis (Lex)

Ariana Richards

Tim

Joseph Mazzelo

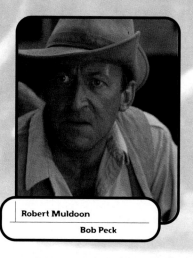

Robert Muldoon

Bob Peck

Donald Gennaro

Martin Ferrero

Cast: JURASSIC PARK

Dr. Alan Grant	....	Sam Neill
Dr. Ellie Slater	....	Laura Dern
Dr. John Hammond	....	Lord Richard Attenborough
Dr. Ian Malcolm	....	Jeff Goldblum
Alexis (Lex)	....	Ariana Richards
Tim	....	Joseph Mazzelo
Robert Muldoon	....	Bob Peck
Donald Gennaro	....	Martin Ferrero
Dr. Wu	....	B.D.Wong
John Arnold	....	Samuel L. Jackson
Dennis Nedry	....	Wayne Knight

Dennis Nedry
Wayne Knight

Shoot her!
Shoot her!

ISLA NUBLAR,
120 miles west of Costa Rica.

Isla Nublar, 120 miles west of Costa Rica.

In the clearing of the jungle a group of heavily armed men stand staring at the trees. The noise grows louder and the expectancy rises in the warm night air.

The trees wave wildly as the large vehicle, its lifting forks extended, crashes into the clearing. It carries a large metal crate. Orders are barked by the grim-faced Robert Muldoon as the vehicle moves into position in front of a huge, secure pen, a watchtower stands in one corner and searchlights beam all around its perimeter.

The crate is lowered and a group of men begin to push it towards a large, closed gate. Agitated sounds come from within the crate. A sharp, strange bark and the men jerk back, clearly frightened. Again they push the crate forward. A man is ordered on top of the crate and negotiates to open the pen's heavy gate from above.

Suddenly there's a huge roar as the gate opens and something heavy and dangerous is in motion. The man screams and falls. Pandemonium reigns. Men rush towards the crate, their heavy-duty weapons cocked and ready.

The shocked man is being dragged by some incredible force towards the pens' interior. They try to save him, they are clearly no match – whatever it is that pulls him towards his doom, it is far too strong. Muldoon screams orders above the chaos. Through the slats of the crate can be seen a large, yellow, inhuman eye darting back and forth. "Shoot her!, shoot her!" Muldoon cries above the noise of panic. It's too late, the damage is done.

Mano de Dios Amber Mine, Dominican Republic.

Donald Gennaro, dressed in a spotless lightweight suit that would look more in place in a top New York restaurant on a hot summer's day, jumps from the small boat, briefcase in hand. He is greeted by Juan Rostagno. Gennaro immediately begins to complain.

"What is this, Rostagno? We're facing a $20 million lawsuit from the family of that worker and Hammond couldn't even be bothered to see me?" His mood gets no better when Rostagno

Dr. Ellie Slater and Dr. Alan Grant at the excavation in the Badlands of Montana

Dr. John Hammond.

Grant and Hammond discuss
the visit to Isla Nublar.

tells him that Hammond had to leave early to be by his daughter's side, who happens to be getting divorced.

He bites back, "We'd be well advised to deal with this situation now. The insurance company thinks …" Gennaro is cut short by a mine worker who rushes up to Rostagno.

"Mosquito, encontramos otra," he spits out and they follow the worker up the hillside towards a cave.

Gennaro continues telling Rostagno that the underwriters are unhappy about the accident raising questions about the park and that the investors are anxious. He tells him that he's promised a thorough inspection.

"Hammond hates inspections. They slow everything down," Rostagno replies and Gennaro shoots back by telling him that having the funding withdrawn would really slow him down.

They enter the cave, Gennaro, banging his head into the wooden props, continues "If two experts sign off the island the insurance guys'll back off. I already got Ian Malcolm, but they think he's too trendy. They want Alan Grant."

"Grant? You'll never get him out of Montana."

"Why not?"

"Because he's like me. He's a digger," and with that Rostagno raises the amber against the light and he gazes upon a perfectly formed mosquito entombed within.

Hammond makes Grant an
offer he can't refuse

🦕 The Badlands of Montana, near Snakewater, USA

A careful excavation is taking place. Dust is being brushed from arcs of fossilised bone. Dr Alan Grant and Dr Ellie Sattler, mid thirties and late twenties respectfully, work together harmoniously. They discuss the merits of their finds and try to reason out theories about tenontosaurus bones and long dead velociraptors.

A voice calls them and says they're ready to try again, Grant mutters something about hating computers, drops the claw they've found into his back pocket, and they walk back to the main dig. It's full of activity, dozens of volunteers working away over a large area. A machine, the 'thumper,' which looks like a large upright vacuum cleaner, bounces into the ground and as many people as possible crowd round a computer situated under a makeshift canvas. The radar from the 'thumper' is shot into the bone in the ground and bounces signals back to the computer – the screen comes alive. A dinosaur skeleton has appeared. Grant looks dismayed when someone mentions that after a few more years of development there'll be no need for digging.

Grant points out that it's a velociraptor, five or six feet high, about nine feet long. He touches the screen to emphasise a point and the machine beeps, the image changes.

⟶

Louis Dodgson and Dennis Nedry discuss embryos in Costa Rica.

SAN JOSE, COSTA RICA.

"That's when the attack comes — not from the front, no, from the side, from the other two raptors you didn't even know were there."

"What did you do?" someone asks.

"He touched it. Dr. Grant is not machine compatible," Ellie remarks.

"They've got it in for me," Grant mutters as one of the volunteers touches the screen and the image comes back on. Grant continues, a little away from the machine now, "Look at the half-moon shaped bone in the wrist. No wonder these guys learned how to fly." Some of the group laugh, Grant is surprised and carries on, "Now, seriously, show of hands. How many of you have read my book?" Ellie and one volunteer raise their hands, Grant sighs, "Maybe dinosaurs have more in common with present day birds than reptiles. Look at the pubic bone – it's turned backwards, just like birds. The vertebrae – full of hollows and air sacs, just like birds. Even the word 'raptor' means 'bird of prey'."

He is rudely interrupted by a plump boy, "That doesn't look very scary. More like a six-foot turkey."

The volunteers all fall silent as Grant, clearly annoyed, walks over to the boy. "Try to imagine yourself in the Jurassic period. You'd get your first look at the six-foot turkey as you move into a clearing. But the raptor, he knew you were there a long time ago. He moves like a bird, lightly, bobbing his head. And you keep still, because you think maybe his visual acuity's based on movement, like a T-rex, and he'll lose you if you don't move. But no, not velociraptor. You stare at him, and he just stares back. That's when the attack comes – not from the front, no, from the side, from the other two raptors you didn't even know were there. Velociraptor's a pack hunter, you see, he uses co-ordinated attack patterns, and he's out in force today. And he slashes at you with this," the boy finds himself with a

The helicopter lands at Isla Nublar.

Dr. Ian Malcolm.

The visitors cannot believe their eyes in Jurassic Park.

The brontosaurus feeds as Hammond, Ellie and Grant look on.

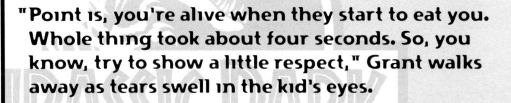

"Point is, you're alive when they start to eat you. Whole thing took about four seconds. So, you know, try to show a little respect," Grant walks away as tears swell in the kid's eyes.

claw very close to his face, "a six inch retractable claw, like a razor on the middle toe. They don't bother to bite the jugular, like a lion, they just slash here, here," Grant moves the claw across the chest and thigh, "or maybe across the belly, spilling your intestines. Point is, you're alive when they start to eat you. Whole thing took about four seconds. So, you know, try to show a little respect," Grant walks away as tears swell in the kid's eyes.

Ellie catches up with Grant, telling him if he wanted to scare the kid he could have pulled a gun on him. Grant, clearly not a lover of children, and Ellie, clearly someone who wants children, have a mildly heated, not too serious, discussion – about children.

Suddenly the sound of a helicopter interrupts them and they look to see it descending on the camp. Canvasses are blown off and dust flies everywhere causing chaos and confusion. Grant runs to the helicopter demanding to know who's responsible, he is pointed towards his own trailer.

Grant bursts in just as a champagne cork pops, his champagne taken from the ancient refrigerator. A white haired, white bearded and white suited elderly gentleman with a walking cane, greets him with a beaming smile. He stops Grant dead in his tracks when he announces that he is John Hammond. He looks around the trailer at the many bones present, obviously approving of the work that has been achieved.

"I see my fifty thousand a year has been well spent," he smiles at Grant.

"Okay, who's the jerk?" the door slams open again as Ellie crashes in. Grant makes the introductions and Ellie is as taken aback as Grant was.

Hammond, not a man to beat about the bush, begins to tell the couple what the purpose of the visit is. About the island he owns off the coast of Costa Rica. How he has spent five years setting up a preserve there. How his investors insist on outside opinions and how he needs the endorsement of two experts, such as Grant and Ellie, before he can open the park to the public. He has never once mentioned what kind of park it is. When questioned he merely smiles and invites the couple over for the weekend – there's a jet standing by at Choteau.

"That wouldn't be possible. We've just discovered a new skeleton and …" Grant explains.

> **"Seven fifty," Dodgson says in a business-like manner, "On delivery, fifty thousand more for each viable embryo. That's a million five, total. If you get all fifteen species off the island." "I'll get 'em all," Nedry acknowledges.**

"I could compensate you by fully funding your dig," Hammond interrupts.
"This would be an awfully unusual time …" Grant continues.
"For three years," Hammond secures the deal.

San Jose, Costa Rica.

Dennis Nedry, late thirties, overweight, sits eating his breakfast outside a cafe, cramming food into his boyish face. He stops eating as a taxi pulls up and Louis Dodgson, ten years older than Dennis and smartly dressed, alights from the cab clutching his attaché case safely to his body.

Nedry cheerfully calls him over by name. Dodgson rebukes him for using his name and Nedry laughs and shouts, "Dodgson!" loudly several times – no one takes any notice. Dodgson, clearly not on the same wavelength with Nedry's humour, slides the case across the table. Nedry's face lights up and he hugs the case like a child hugs a long-awaited Christmas gift.

"Seven fifty," Dodgson says in a business-like manner, "On delivery, fifty thousand more for each viable embryo. That's a million five, total. If you get all fifteen species off the island."

"I'll get 'em all," Nedry acknowledges.

"Remember – viable embryos. They're no use to us if they don't survive," Dodgson emphasises the point. He then answers Nedry's question about transporting the embryos by pulling what looks like an ordinary can of shaving cream from his travelling bag. He explains that the bottom slides open and that the embryos can be placed in the cool, secret compartment, the can still functions normally. Dodgson continues to tell him that the coolant gas will last for thirty six hours and that he has until then to get the embryos back to San Jose. Nedry reminds him that it's up to his man on the boat to be ready at seven o'clock the following night, at the east dock.

"How you planning to beat the security?" Dodgson inquires.

"I got an eighteen minute window. Eighteen minutes and your company catches up on ten years of research," Nedry confidentially tells Dodgson as a waiter arrives with the

Donald Gennaro.

A wondrous sight in Jurassic Park.

The Visitor Centre, Jurassic Park.

WHEN DINOSAURS RULED THE EARTH

Inside the spectacular lobby.

Nedry makes a point of looking at the cheque and then into Dodgson's eyes, "Don't get cheap on me, Dodgson — that was Hammond's mistake. Dodgson takes care of the cheque.

cheque. Nedry makes a point of looking at the cheque and then into Dodgson's eyes, "Don't get cheap on me, Dodgson – that was Hammond's mistake." Dodgson takes care of the cheque.

The Pacific Ocean

The 'In-Gen Construction' logo features strongly on the side of the helicopter that flies low over the Pacific. Hammond sits with legs apart, both hands atop his cane planted firmly between his legs, like some ancient mystic. Grant and Ellie sit next to him, opposite are the lawyer, Donald Gennaro, now dressed more suitably, but still looking out of place in his designer safari suit and Dr. Ian Malcolm. Malcolm is around forty, swarthy, thick black hair, shades, a black leather jacket cut like a normal coat and a manner that some would call charismatic and others downright annoying.

He addresses Grant and Ellie, but it is clear his main interest is aimed at Ellie, "So you two dig up dinosaurs?"

Grant, who has clearly not taken to Malcolm, grunts, "Try to," under his breath, causing Dr. Malcolm to laugh in a strange maniacal way.

"You'll have to get used to Dr. Malcolm! He has a deplorable excess of personality – especially for a mathematician!" Hammond tries to make all concerned feel more comfortable.

"Chaotician, chaotician actually. John doesn't subscribe to chaos, particularly what it has to say about his little science project." Malcolm is clearly not a man to keep quiet, especially when you want him to.

Hammond snorts, "Codswollop! You've never come close to explaining these concerns of yours about the island!"

"I certainly have! Very clearly! Because of the behaviour of the system in phase space!" Malcolm replies, clearly enjoying the exchanges.

"Bunch of fashionable number crunching, that's all it is!" Hammond is clearly frustrated.

John Hammond prepares to present his vision of Jurassic Park.

Malcolm turns to Grant and Ellie, "Dr. Grant, Dr. Sattler – you've heard of Chaos Theory?" they clearly haven't, "Non-linear equations? Strange attractors?" they shake their heads as Malcolm points directly at Ellie, "Dr. Sattler, I refuse to believe that you are not familiar with the concept of attraction!" Ellie smiles and squirms, Grant is clearly not impressed.

Hammond, equally unimpressed, turns to Gennaro, "I bring scientists – you bring a rock star."

The conversation is stopped dead in it's tracks as Hammond, clearly excited, points out of the window. Isla Nublar, Hammond's very own island – tall, lush, tropical trees and a hint of mystery. The helicopter descends and makes it's way into the island, the helicopter bouncing up and down as the wind gets under it. Hammond, smiling like a Cheshire cat, explains about the wind shears and the planned airstrip as the others hurriedly fasten their seat-belts. Grant can't get his to fasten, Malcolm effortlessly does his, chews gum and grins at the harassed Grant.

Jurassic Park

The helicopter descends opposite a huge, spectacular water-fall. It lands on a circular piece of rock with a white cross firmly painted on it. The doors are opened for them, Hammond steps down and surveys his island with wonderment, the others follow. Two open-topped waiting jeeps, with the logo 'Jurassic Park' emblazoned on their sides, transport the travellers along a dusty, bumpy road.

They arrive at a thirty foot high electrified fence, attendants close the large gate behind them. Gennaro, travelling with Hammond, his eyes sweep along the fence, "The full fifty miles of perimeter fence are in place?"

"And the concrete moats, and the motion sensor tracking systems. Try to enjoy yourself, Donald," Hammond cheerfully tells him.

Gennaro is obviously not here to enjoy himself, "Let's get something straight, John. This is no weekend excursion, this is a serious investigation of the stability of the island because your investors, whom I represent, are deeply concerned. Forty-eight hours from now if they aren't convinced, I'm not convinced – I'll shut you down, John."

"Forty-eight hours from now, Donald, I'll be accepting your apology!" Hammond, cheerful as ever, tells him straight.

The jeeps travel across open grasslands, broken only by a variety of exotic trees. Hammond orders the jeeps to stop. Ellie continues to talk loudly to Grant as she studies a large, supposedly extinct leaf that she has pulled from the foliage along the way.

Grant, ignores her, suddenly staring out of the car and then slowly standing up, he removes his shades because he cannot believe what he is now seeing. He grips the top of Ellie's head and swivels it round so that she too can gaze at the huge brontosaurus that towers above them, moving

Watching the birth of a dinosaur.

**Ellie: "T-T-rex, you said you got a T-rex,"
Hammond: "We've got a T-rex,"
Grant: "Say it again."
Hammond: "We've got a T-rex."**

slowly and with unexpected grace amongst the tall trees. Standing some thirty-five feet tall, it's long arching neck allows it to easily eat the leaves from the tops of the trees.

They all just stare in disbelief except for Hammond who proudly beams at the others. Ellie and Grant step from the jeep and walk towards the dinosaur, pointing and discussing the finer points of what they still cannot come to terms with.

Malcolm, a huge grin on his face, mutters "You did it. You crazy son of a bitch, you did it."

Gennaro, sitting alongside him, dollar signs almost in his eyes says, "We're gonna make a fortune with this place."

Hammond joins Ellie and Grant, their necks craned upwards. Grant asks him how fast it is, Hammond, unsure says "Uh – well we clocked the T-rex at thirty-two miles an hour."

"T-T-rex, you said you got a T-rex," Ellie, if it's possible, is even more amazed.

"We've got a T-rex," confirms Hammond as Grant grabs him by the shoulders.

"Say it again."

"We've got a T-rex," Hammond nonchalantly tells Grant. Grant walks away almost doubled in sheer disbelief. Ellie goes to him, almost comforting him into believing this is all true.

"Dr. Grant – welcome to Jurassic Park," Hammond looks further across the plain. Ellie and Grant, in each others arms, follow his gaze. A whole herd of dinosaurs can be seen in the distance.

"They're moving in herds – they do move in herds," Grant says to himself and then to Hammond, "How did you do this?" Hammond replies that he'll show them and reluctantly they leave for the jeeps and the main compound of Jurassic Park.

The main compound is an impressive area of several structures connected by walkways and surrounded by 20 foot high fencing. The jungle almost surrounds it. The visitor's centre dominates the compound and this where the jeeps finally drop off their occupants. Inside the still unfinished lobby of the tall building, workers on scaffolding are assembling dinosaur skeletons, hanging from cables attached to the high ceiling. A huge tyrannosaurus rex dominates. A banner hangs with the legend 'Welcome to Jurassic Park,' greeting all who enter.

Lunch isn't going well for John Hammond.

The guests debate the ethics of Jurassic Park.

> "... the most advanced amusement park in the entire world, combining all the latest technologies ...
> We've made living biological attractions so astonishing they'll capture the imagination of the entire world."

Hammond is in full swing, "... the most advanced amusement park in the entire world, combining all the latest technologies and I'm not just talking about rides, you know. Everybody has rides. We've made living biological attractions so astonishing they'll capture the imagination of the entire world." Ellie and Grant look around as they mount the staircase towards another wing.

"So what are you thinking," Ellie asks Grant.

"That we're out of a job," Grant replies.

"Don't you mean extinct?" Ian Malcolm quips.

Grant, Ellie, Malcolm and Gennaro follow Hammond into a small, but impressive auditorium. Hammond walks towards the stage just as an image of himself appears on the screen.

The image greets the real John Hammond "Hello John!" Hammond fumbles in his shirt pocket for a small card with his lines written on it. The image carries on, "Fine, I guess. But how did I get here?"

"Here, let me show you. First, I'll need a drop of blood, your blood!" Hammond is with it now, growing in confidence as the large image of himself extends his finger and Hammond pretends to prick it.

"Ouch! That hurts, John!"

"Relax, John. It's all part of the miracle of cloning!" Hammond steps back as his image on the screen multiplies, Hammond after Hammond stepping out from the back of the original image.

"Cloning from what? Loy extraction has never recreated an intact DNA strand!" Grant whispers to Ellie and Malcolm.

"Not without massive sequence gaps!" Malcolm clearly states.

"Paleo-DNA? From what source? Where do you get 100 million year old dinosaur blood?" Ellie asks no-one in particular as they again concentrate on the screen.

A cartoon character, Mr. DNA has joined the image of Hammond on the screen. He replies to

Lex and Tim greet Grandpa.

> **"A DNA strand like me is a blueprint for building a living thing! And sometimes animals that went extinct millions of years ago, like dinosaurs, left their blueprints behind for us to find! We just had to know where to look!"**

The guests prepare to leave on their excursion.

Hammond's question of where did he come from by informing him, in a Texas drawl, that he came from his blood. And that just one drop of blood contains billions of strands of DNA – the building blocks of life. It has now clearly turned into Mr. DNA's show. Using film stock, graphics and animation on the screen, Mr DNA explains:

"A DNA strand like me is a blueprint for building a living thing! And sometimes animals that went extinct millions of years ago, like dinosaurs, left their blueprints behind for us to find! We just had to know where to look! A hundred million years ago, there were mosquitoes, just like today. And, just like today, they fed on the blood of animals – even dinosaurs. Sometimes, after biting a dinosaur the mosquito would land on the branch of a tree and get stuck in the sap! After a long time, the tree sap would get hard and become fossilised, just like a dinosaur bone, preserving the mosquito inside." The screen now shows a science lab, buzzing with activity and close ups of microscopic work on a mosquito, trapped in amber, taking place as Mr. DNA continues, "This fossilised tree sap, which we call amber, waited for millions of years with the mosquitoes inside – until Jurassic Park's scientists came along! Using sophisticated techniques, they extract the preserved blood from the mosquito, and – Bingo! Dino DNA." A long needle has been inserted into the amber and into the thorax of the mosquito, making an extraction.

Mr. DNA continues excitedly to explain that a full DNA strand contains three billion genetic codes and how specially developed Thinking Machine Supercomputers and gene sequences can break the strand down in minutes and that Virtual Reality displays can show the geneticists the gaps in the DNA sequence. He explains most animal DNA is 90% identical and by using the complete DNA of a frog, and inserting the missing 10% he triumphantly concludes, "Now we can make a baby dinosaur!" as an animated dinosaur

Tim.

bursts out from a large egg.

"Dum dum dum – a march or something, it's not written yet, and the tour moves on," Hammond, now sitting behind his guests, concludes the screening. He throws a switch and large circular bars, attached to the seats drop over everyone's legs securing them in position. The whole rows of seats move and finally come to rest in front a large hi-tech science lab where white-coated technicians are busily at work. Unfertilised ostrich or emu eggs, where the dinosaur DNA takes place, are carefully handled. As Gennaro sycophantically tells Hammond how overwhelming it all is, the three others, sitting in front, bark questions at Hammond.

"Wait a minute! How do you interrupt the cellular mitosis?"

"Can't we see the unfertilised host eggs?"

Malcolm counts to three and he, Ellie and Grant shove the bars off and make for the lab. Hammond follows them with Gennaro in tow. Hammond now leads them into the hatchery where Grant heads straight for a round incubator table covered in straw – and large eggs. A robotic arm carefully turns the eggs round for correct exposure to the light shining brightly above.

An Asian-American technician greets Hammond and announces that one of the eggs is ready to hatch as Grant leans forward, staring intently at the now moving egg. The others gather round, fascinated.

"Henry, why didn't you tell me? You know I insist on being here when they're born," Hammond tells the technician. The shell begins slowly to crack and the life form within can just be seen. The baby dinosaur struggles to get out, Hammond talks to it like a cooing midwife, gently urging it out of the shell. He helps the dinosaur by breaking tiny bits of the shell away.

"They imprint on the first living thing they come into contact with. It helps them trust me. I've been present for the birth of every little creature on this island," Hammond now gently strokes the new born baby.

"Surely not the ones that have bred in the wild?" Malcolm asks.

Henry Wu, the technician replies, "Actually they can't breed in the wild. Population control is one of our security precautions. There is no unauthorised breeding in Jurassic Park."

"How do you know they can't breed?" Malcolm asks.

"Because all the animals in Jurassic Park are female. We engineered them that way," Wu smiles as the animal is now free and the subject of much adoration and discussion. Malcolm is still not convinced and demands to know how they know

Examining a sick triceratops.

they're all female – does someone lift up their skirts? Wu carefully explains that their chromosomes are controlled and that all the vertebrate embryos are inherently female – the extra hormone needed to create the male is denied at the right stage of development.

Malcolm remains unconvinced. "John, the kind of control you're attempting is not possible. If there's one thing that the history of evolution has taught us, it's that life will not be contained, life breaks free. It expands to new territories, it crashes through barriers. Painfully, perhaps even dangerously, but there it is … there it is."

"You're implying that a group composed entirely of female animals will breed?" It's Wu's turn now to ask the question.

"No. I'm simply saying that life – finds a way," Malcolm gives them all something to think about for a while.

Grant is now holding the tiny baby in the palms of his hands, he cannot keep his eyes away from it – seemingly transfixed. He finally looks up and asks Wu to confirm what he is already thinking, hoping to be proved to be wrong, "What species is this?"

"It's a velociraptor," answers Wu, somewhat hesitantly.

Grant looks down again at the seemingly innocent tiny baby in his hands and barely gets the words out, "You bred raptors?"

Grant stands in front of the heavily fortified raptor pen – the scene of the accident some time before. He glares grimly as a steer is hoisted by a crane into the air. Hammond and the others join him. Hammond explains that he intended to show them the raptors later after lunch, a lunch despite Hammond's glowing praise for the cook, that Grant is clearly not interested in. They all climb the stairs to the observation track and look down at the foliage. The steer is lowered into the pen as they all wait, quietly – waiting for something to happen.

It is the sudden sound of the steer being torn apart that they hear. Sickening sounds of flesh being ripped away and bone crunching, stomach turning noises, screams and growls the like of which they will never want to hear again.

"They should all be destroyed," it is the British voice of Robert Muldoon, as grim faced now as he was at the time of

Ellie makes a diagnosis.

TRICERATOPS

the accident at this very place.

"Robert Muldoon was my game warden in Kenya. Bit of an alarmist, but he's dealt with the raptors more than anyone," Hammond says by way of an introduction.

Grant shakes his hand "What kind of metabolism do they have? What's their growth rate?"

"They're lethal at eight months. And I do mean lethal. I've hunted everything that can hunt you, but the way these things move ..."

"Fast for a biped?"

"Cheetah speed. Fifty, sixty miles an hour if they ever got out in the open. And they're astonishing jumpers," Muldoon concludes.

"Yes, yes, yes that's why we're taking extreme precautions. The viewing area below us will have eight-inch tempered glass set in reinforced steel frames ..." Hammond tries to reassure everyone.

Grant carries on his conversation with Muldoon, ignoring Hammond, "Do they show intelligence? With a brain cavity like theirs we assumed ..."

"They show extreme intelligence, even problem solving intelligence. Especially the big one. We bred eight originally, but when she came in she took over the pride and killed all but two of the others. That one – when she looks at you, you can see she's working things out. That's why we have to feed 'em like this. She had them all attacking the fences when the feeders came," Muldoon explains.

Ellie asks, "But the fences are electrified, right?"

"That's right, but they never attack the same place twice. They were testing the fences for weaknesses, systematically. They remember," Muldoon answers, solemnly.

The crane whirr's behind them, the cable bearing what's left of the bloody harness comes into view. Hammond rubs his hands together, "Yes, well, who's hungry?"

Hammond, Grant, Ellie, Malcolm and Gennaro sit down at a long dining table as lunch is served. Slides show up all around the darkened room and a recorded voice describes various features, present and future, of the park. Hammond himself tells the others that the park will open with the basic tour and will be followed by other spectacular rides and attractions in six to twelve months time. Gennaro, now completely enjoying the weekend, enthuses about the amount

"Don't you see the danger inherent in what you're doing here? Genetic power is the most awesome force this planet has ever seen, but you wield it like a kid that's found his dad's gun."

of revenue that can be made, he sees it all as a licence to print money, his enthusiasm is only slightly dampened when Hammond reminds him that Jurassic Park was not built for the super rich and that everyone in the world's got a right to enjoy the dinosaurs. Gennaro's suggestion for a 'coupon day' goes down like a lead balloon with Dr. Ian Malcolm.

"The lack of humility before nature that has been displayed here staggers me," he states, flatly.

"Thank you, Dr. Malcolm, but I think things are a little different than you and I feared," Gennaro retorts.

"Yes, they are. They're a lot worse," Malcolm glumly replies as Gennaro begins to squabble. Hammond cuts him short and insists he wants to hear all viewpoints, allowing Malcolm to continue, "Don't you see the danger inherent in what you're doing here? Genetic power is the most awesome force this planet has ever seen, but you wield it like a kid that's found his dad's gun," Malcolm, in full swing now rides roughshod over Gennaro as he tries to interrupt, "I'll tell you the problem with the scientific power that you're using here. It didn't require any discipline to attain it – you read what others have done and you took the next step. You didn't earn the knowledge for yourselves so you don't take any responsibility for it. You simply stood on the shoulders of geniuses to accomplish something as fast as you could and before you even knew what you had, you've patented it and packaged it and slapped it on a plastic lunchbox and now you're selling it, selling it!" Malcolm bangs the table to emphasise his point.

Hammond, coolly and calmly replies to Malcolm's outburst, "You don't give us our due credit. Our scientists have done things no one could ever do before."

Malcolm and Grant – the calm before the storm.

Alarm in the control room.

The T-rex tears through the electric fence.

Tim cannot believe his eyes.

> **"Hold on — this is no species that was obliterated by deforestation or the building of a dam. Dinosaurs had their shot and nature selected them for extinction."**

Lex looks on in horror.

"Yeah, but your scientists were so preoccupied with whether or not they could that they didn't stop to think if they should," Malcolm replies.

"Condors are on the verge of extinction, if I was to create a flock of condors on this island – you wouldn't have anything to say," Hammond, getting a little angry now, points at Malcolm.

"Hold on – this is no species that was obliterated by deforestation or the building of a dam. Dinosaurs had their shot and nature selected them for extinction," Malcolm believes he is clearly right.

Hammond shakes his head, "I don't understand this Luddite attitude, especially from a scientist. How could we stand in the light of discovery and not act?"

"What's so great about discovery? It's a violent, penetrative act that scars what it explores. What you call discovery I call the rape of the natural world," Malcolm says, defiantly.

Ellie gets drawn in, "Well, the question is – how much can you know anything about an extinct system? And therefore how could you ever assume that you can control it. There are plants, for example, right here in your restaurant, that are poisonous. You picked them because they're pretty, but these are aggressive living things that have no idea what century they're living in and will defend themselves. Violently if necessary."

Hammond is now getting rattled, it's not going as it should, "Dr. Grant, if there's one person who can appreciate what I'm trying to do."

Grant studies for a moment, leaning forward, "The world has just changed so radically and we're all running to catch up. I don't want to jump to any conclusions but look, Dinosaurs and Man, two species separated by sixty-five million years of evolution, have just been suddenly thrown back in the mix together – how can we possibly have the slightest idea of what to expect?"

The T-rex stares at its prey.

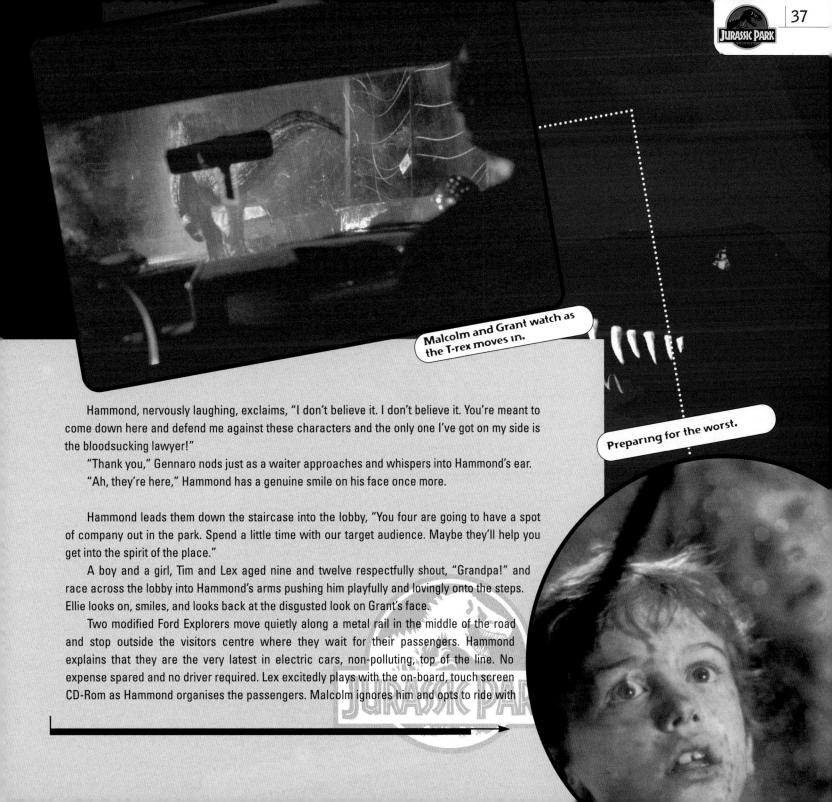

Malcolm and Grant watch as the T-rex moves in.

Preparing for the worst.

Hammond, nervously laughing, exclaims, "I don't believe it. I don't believe it. You're meant to come down here and defend me against these characters and the only one I've got on my side is the bloodsucking lawyer!"

"Thank you," Gennaro nods just as a waiter approaches and whispers into Hammond's ear.

"Ah, they're here," Hammond has a genuine smile on his face once more.

Hammond leads them down the staircase into the lobby, "You four are going to have a spot of company out in the park. Spend a little time with our target audience. Maybe they'll help you get into the spirit of the place."

A boy and a girl, Tim and Lex aged nine and twelve respectfully shout, "Grandpa!" and race across the lobby into Hammond's arms pushing him playfully and lovingly onto the steps. Ellie looks on, smiles, and looks back at the disgusted look on Grant's face.

Two modified Ford Explorers move quietly along a metal rail in the middle of the road and stop outside the visitors centre where they wait for their passengers. Hammond explains that they are the very latest in electric cars, non-polluting, top of the line. No expense spared and no driver required. Lex excitedly plays with the on-board, touch screen CD-Rom as Hammond organises the passengers. Malcolm ignores him and opts to ride with

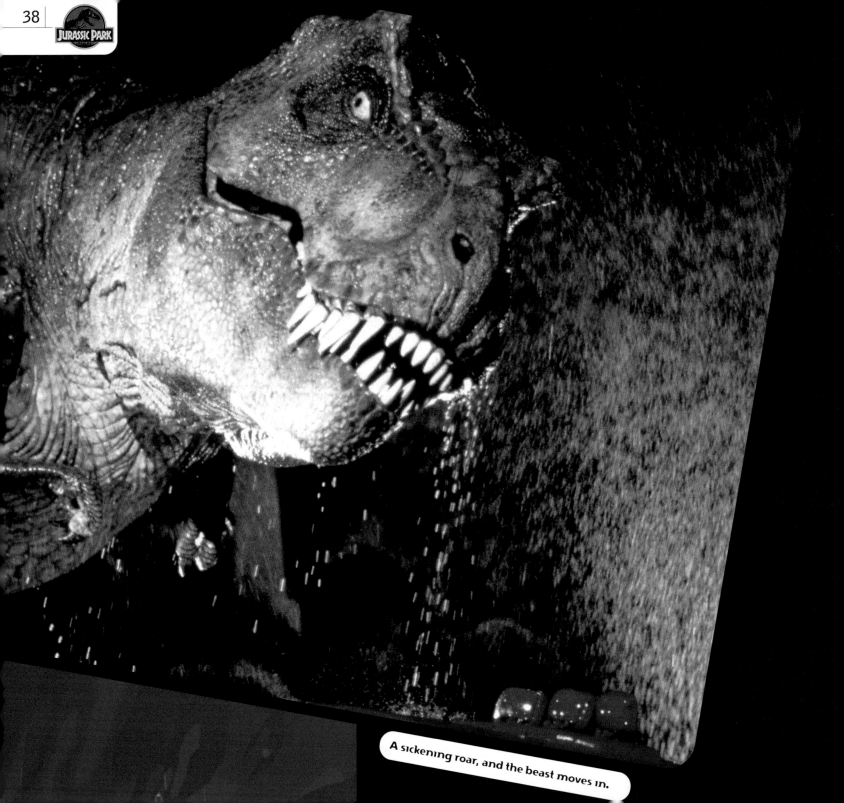

A sickening roar, and the beast moves in.

"You really think dinosaurs turned into birds? And that's where all the dinosaurs went?"

Ellie causing Grant some dismay. Hammond announces he'll be watching from the control room and leaves.

Grant heads towards Ellie and Malcolm in the second Explorer in line when he comes face to face with a grinning Tim, "I read your book."

"Oh. That's, er – great," Grant, uncomfortable, grunts and side-steps him.

Tim follows. "You really think dinosaurs turned into birds? And that's where all the dinosaurs went?"

"Well, a few species may have evolved, along those lines …"Grant climbs into the rear car as Tim follows him.

"Because they sure don't look like birds to me. I heard a meteor hit the earth and made like this one hundred mile crater down in Mexico or someplace and that's how come they stopped."

"Which car were you planning on?" Grant asks the boy. Tim shrugs, so Grant goes to the car in front, gets in as Tim follows, still rattling on about dinosaur theories. Grant moves across the seat and out of the other door – closing it and cutting Tim off mid-sentence. He walks back to the other car and straight into Lex who points at the grinning Ellie and says "She said I should ride with you, because it would be good for you."Grant nods, not amused.

The control room is full of the latest hi-tech computer equipment and dozens of video screens showing areas of the park. It's like mission control for a space launch, only it's for monitoring and controlling dinosaur activity. Hammond and Muldoon sweep in. Muldoon, a computer read-out in his hand, informs Hammond that a tropical storm line is seventy-five miles west. Hammond sighs, mutters something about building the park in Orlando and moves towards the main console as Muldoon tells him the storm may swing south like the last one.

They reach the main console, where Ray Arnold, a forty year-old, chain-smoking, African-American sits, headset in position. Hammond nervously pats Arnold on the back, "Ray, Start the tour program."

A large yellow eye stares into the car.

The T-rex lunges, smashing the plexiglass roof.

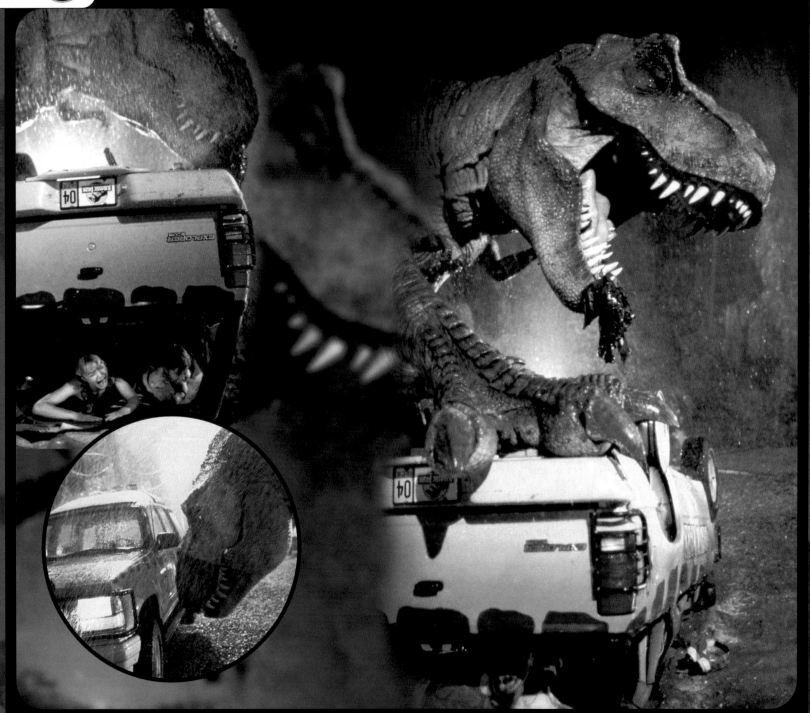

The frenzied attack.

> **"We've got all the problems of a major theme park and a major zoo, and the computer's not even on it's feet yet."**

"Hold onto your butts," Ray announces as he presses the computer key. They watch the electric cars on the monitors move forward as Hammond sighs, he's been waiting a long time for this.

The driverless cars move forward amid great excitement. A voice-over blares out relevant information and they eventually reach two huge wooden gates reminiscent of those used in the "King Kong" movie – a fact Malcolm is quick to point out, "What they got in there, King Kong?" At the top of the gates a sign reads, 'Welcome to Jurassic Park.'

Hammond's voice from the control room comes over the speaker, "The voice you're now hearing is Richard Tiling. We spared no expense!"

The passengers of both cars press against the windows to get a better look as the voice tells them, "If you look to the right, you will see a herd of the first dinosaurs on our tour, called dilophosaurus." They see nothing whatsoever, the voice continues with a detailed description, ignored by the disappointed passengers.

In the control room Ray Arnold, Hammond leaning over his shoulder, glares at the computer screen. Arnold, ever present cigarette dangling from his lips, is clearly not happy "Vehicle headlights are on and are not responding. Those shouldn't be running off the car batteries. Item fifty-one on today's glitch list. We've got all the problems of a major theme park and a major zoo, and the computer's not even on it's feet yet."

A disappointed Hammond turns round to the large figure of Dennis Nedry, back from his clandestine meeting in San Jose.

He sits slouched in front of a computer drinking soda, "I am totally unappreciated in my time. We can run the whole park from this room, with minimal staff, for up to three days. you think that kind of automation is easy? Or cheap? You know anybody who can network eight Connection Machines and de-bug two million lines of code for what I bid this job? Because I'd sure as hell like to see them try."

Hammond is clearly not interested in Nedry's financial problems and the two have a short heated discussion before Arnold reminds him about the headlights. As Nedry begins to reply

> **"T-rex doesn't want to be fed, he wants to hunt. You can't just suppress sixty-five million years of gut instinct."**

Muldoon turns towards them, annoyed at the squabbling, "Quiet, all of you. They're approaching the tyrannosaur paddock."

Again, as the Explorers reach the paddock and come to a halt, nothing other than lush green can be seen behind the high electrified fence. They silently stare out, expectantly. Malcolm speaks first "God creates dinosaurs. God destroys dinosaurs. God creates man. Man destroys God. Man creates dinosaurs."

"Dinosaurs eat man. Women inherit the Earth," Ellie replies as Malcolm and Grant stare at her.

Arnold's voice comes over the speaker, they are going to tempt the rex. Everyone stares through the fence as a small cage rises up into view, hydraulically lifted from beneath the ground. Inside a bleating goat is chained to a stake. The cage bars drop down. Lex is obviously not happy with the goat's fate. Tim on the other hand grins widely and Gennaro asks Lex if she's never had lamb chops. Lex informs him that she's a vegetarian.

In the other car Grant shakes his head, "T-rex doesn't want to be fed, he wants to hunt. You can't just suppress sixty-five million years of gut instinct."

Nothing happens, nothing until the goat, seemingly as fed up as all the others decides to lay down. Everyone sits back – more disappointment. Malcolm picks up a microphone and talks to the Control Room, "Now, eventually you do plan to have dinosaurs on your dinosaur tour, right?" Hammond, shakes his head between his hands and announces to no one in particular that he really hates that man.

The cars move and Malcolm, getting all too familiar with Ellie, begins to expound on his chaos theory pointing out that the tyronnosaur obeys no set patterns or park schedules. He rattles on to a confused Ellie about unpredictability and the comparisons to what's happening in the park. Grant, oblivious to what he probably would consider nonsense anyway, stares out of the window, sensing something is out in that field. He simply has to see it. He jerks open the door, as Malcolm seductively turns the chaos theory into chance meetings with someone and how the course of your future can be changed, and Grant is out of the moving car.

Grant lights a flare.

Distracting the T-rex.

Malcolm flees for his life.

> As everyone in the control room scurries about Dennis Nedry can afford to look at the image now on his monitor, the image of a steel door labelled 'Embryonic Cold Storage. Restricted!'

"See! I'm right again! No one could have predicted that Dr. Grant would suddenly jump out of a moving vehicle!" Ellie calls after Grant and she too follows him, leaving Malcolm alone in the car, "There's another example! See? Here I am now, by myself, talking to myself – that's Chaos Theory!"

Hammond, Muldoon and Arnold watch the exodus, now from both cars, on the monitors. Hammond barks for the programme to be stopped as Muldoon reminds him that they should have had locking mechanisms on the vehicle doors. As everyone in the control room scurries about Dennis Nedry can afford to look at the image now on his monitor, the image of a steel door labelled 'Embryonic Cold Storage. Restricted!' He looks to another image, a supply ship moored at the east dock. A can of shaving cream sits close by him.

Grant, Ellie, Gennaro, Malcolm and the two children walk through the open park towards some trees as the sky begins to darken. Tim incessantly talks to Grant about dinosaur theories, most of which seem to contradict Grant's own book. Gennaro is unhappy, he clearly thinks they shouldn't be out here. Lex stumbles and Grant catches her by the hand, she won't let go, smiling up at the uncomfortable Grant, Ellie smiles with amusement.

They all stop dead in their tracks. Grant orders everyone to stop where they are and carries on through the long grass, he could have saved his breath, they all follow him. Before them, lying on it's side is a huge triceratops. Two large horns over it's eyes, a third horn over it's nose, enormous curved shell flanking its head, it breathes long and loud.

Grant, Ellie and Tim are the first to reach the animal. The others circle it warily. Gerry Harding, veterinarian, is there explaining it's okay to approach, the beast is sick and has been tranquillised by Muldoon. Grant and Ellie stroke and caress the triceratops, eyes filled with wonder and amazement. They are in heaven.

Ellie moves her loving hands toward it's mouth and sees liquid leaking from blisters on the beast's huge tongue, "Microvesicles. That's interesting," she asks the veterinarian

Grant and Lex freeze in fear.

for his penlight and looks into the animal's eyes. "You have pupillary effects from the tranquillisers?" Ellie asks Harding.

"Yes, miotic, pupils should be constricted," he replies.

"But these pupils are dilated," Ellie tells Harding who checks for himself as Ellie summarises, "That's pharmacological. From local plant life, one would think." She rises and begins to study various pieces of foliage, "Is that West Indian lilac?" she ask Harding as he crouches beside her.

"Yes. We know they're toxic, but the animals don't eat them," Harding replies and confirms when Ellie asks him again.

"Only one way to be positive," Ellie announces as she stands up next to a watching Malcolm, "I'll have to see the dinosaur's droppings."

"Dino … droppings, droppings?" Malcolm stutters and scratches his head.

In the control room Hammond, Muldoon and Arnold are becoming increasingly worried about the weather situation. The monitor shows a bleak picture. Hammond is reluctant but the others insist that the tour must be cut short – it can always continue the following day. As soon as the party get back to the cars they will be told they'll be returning to the centre. Hammond, frustrated, curses.

Malcolm stands before a seven foot high mound of triceratops dung and utters the obvious, "That is one big pile of shit," as Ellie pushes her plastic gloved arm right into the centre of a smaller, slightly less impressive pile.

She pulls out a huge handful and examines it, noting to Harding "You're right. There's no trace of lilac berries. It's so odd though. So she's suffering from Meilia toxicity every six weeks …" she walks away, deep in thought. Malcolm remarks to Grant that Ellie appears to be tenacious, Grant grunts that Malcolm has no idea, leaving him to call out to Ellie, reminding her to wash her hands before eating.

The T-rex senses its prey.

> "So much for our first tour. Two no-shows and a sick triceratops."
> "It could have been worse, John — a lot worse," Ray Arnold takes a long draw on his cigarette, having no idea of what is about to happen.

Dennis Nedry speedily types commands into his console. A red warning box flashes up on the screen, it says 'EXECUTE?'

Grant, Ellie and Tim are once again kneeling before the triceratop, the others look on as the wind begins to get stronger. Gennaro jumps as the sound of thunder crashes, he nervously tells everyone that he must insist they get moving. Ellie says she'll stay with Harding to continue examining the dinosaur for a while longer, Harding agrees and will drop Ellie off at the visitor centre when they've finished. The others make their way back to the cars as lightning crashes in the ever darkening sky.

Dennis Nedry is staring at his monitor with a look of complete shock. The supply boat, so important to his plan, is being rocked by huge, dangerous waves. Nedry can see the mate, rain lashing down, as he talks to him on the deck phone.

"There's nothing I can do! If the Captain says we gotta go, we gotta go!"

Nedry, panicking, pleads "No, no listen – you've gotta give me the time. I did a test run on this thing and it took me twenty minutes, I thought I could maybe push it to eighteen but you've got to give me at least fifteen minutes – give me fifteen minutes."

"No promises!" replies the mate as he slams down the phone.

Arnold tells the others in the control room that the vehicles are on their way back. Hammond sadly reflects, "So much for our first tour. Two no-shows and a sick triceratops."

"It could have been worse, John – a lot worse," Ray Arnold takes a long draw on his cigarette, having no idea of what is about to happen.

Nedry, sweating nervously, stands and asks if any of the others would like a soda and mumbles incoherently about visiting the drinks machine. He tries pulls himself together as the others look at him, "Oh I finished de-bugging the phones, you told me I should, so I did but the system's compiling for eighteen or twenty minutes, so one or two minor systems may switch on and off – it's nothing to worry about." They nod and turn away, Dennis Nedry presses his mouse

Nedry flees the park.

button. The 'Execute?' sign is activated. A stopwatch on the screen counts down from 60 seconds, it is synchronised with his own watch. He leaves the room.

Rain lashes onto the Explorer cars moving steadily along in the black of night. Grant and Malcolm share a hip flask and have a brief discussion about children and wives. Malcolm has three kids, probably has had as many wives and would like another. Grant just hopes he doesn't mean Ellie. The cars roll on.

Nedry, panting, stares at his watch. The sixty seconds are up and the illuminated security lock panel on the door that says 'Embryonic Cold Storage, Restricted!' goes dark. The door is open.

Arnold flips the top of his Zippo, goes to light his cigarette and stops as he informs Hammond that the door security systems are shutting down. Hammond merely reminds him that Dennis Nedry had said a few systems would go off-line.

Nedry has now reached and accessed the tall, thin glass slides. He removes, with great care, the viable embryos labelled, 'Stegosaurus,' 'Apatosaurus,' 'Tyrannosaurus Rex' and others. He puts them into the slots in the compartment at the bottom of the shaving cream can.

As Malcolm turns to Grant once more neither of them notice the video screen, situated in the console, suddenly go off, "By the way, Dr. Sattler wouldn't happen to be – available, is she?"

"Why?" Grant pointedly asks him.

"Oh, I'm sorry. Are you two …" Malcolm continues.

"Yeah," Grant replies as the cars suddenly comes to a stop – the lights in the vehicle go out. Grant looks at his hands, assuming it's his fault, "Hey what did I touch?"

"You didn't touch anything – we stopped," Malcolm looks around worriedly.

Ray Arnold looks surprised at the map of the park on the terminal. Lights surrounding the perimeter are flashing warning signals, "Fences are falling all over the park! A few minor systems – he said!"

Hammond barks at Muldoon, "Find Nedry! Check the vending machines."

Nedry drives the jeep to the huge 'King Kong' gates and jumps down. He splashes towards a control panel, throws open the small door and pulls down the manual override switch. He gets back in the car and forces the gates open with the car as he drives through, he speeds into the park grounds, no time to waste.

The inquisitive dilophosaur eyes Nedry.

He looks at his watch, time is running out for Dennis Nedry.

Arnold, Hammond and Muldoon gather round the absent Nedry's terminal. Muldoon, now very concerned asks Arnold if the raptor fences are out. Arnold, thankfully tells him they're still on. Hammond asks why the hell would Nedry turn the others off?

A panting Dennis Nedry hurriedly shoves open a large metal door marked 'Danger! Electrified Fence! This Door Cannot Be Opened When Fence Is Armed.' He gets back into the car and drives through the gate and into the deep mud of the road. He can hardly see through the windscreen as the storm lashes down, he can hardly see through his spectacles which he constantly wipes as they begin to steam up. He looks at his watch, time is running out for Dennis Nedry. He hits the brakes as an unexpected fork in the road looms up. The jeep skids into a signpost. Nedry gets out and looks at the sign swinging on the nail, an arrow points at the floor. The sign above it reads 'East Docks.' Dennis Nedry is lost. He takes the road to the left.

Hammond and Muldoon lean over Arnold as he tries command after command to 'access main program grid.' All he gets for his pains is a 'permission denied' and a gross, finger-waving cartoon image of Nedry appears telling him he didn't say the magic word.

Arnold is furious, "Please. God damn it! I hate this hacker crap!"

Hammond tells Arnold to call Nedry's people in Cambridge and Arnold picks up the nearest phone – the phones are dead. Hammond turns to Muldoon, "Where did the vehicles stop?"

Outside the tyrannosaurus paddock the forgotten goat bleats on and on. Grant runs back from the first car and gets back in the car with Malcolm, telling him immediately that the other car's radio is out of action as well.

In the car up front Tim and Lex sit in the back, Gennaro in front. Tim, bored, looks under the seat and comes up with a pair of large, padded goggles.

He is very excited by his find despite Gennaro telling him that "If they're heavy, they're expensive, put them down."

"Nice boy, nice dinosaur ..."

Nedry is unaware of its evil intent.

As night closes in, a breathtaking sight greets Grant, Lex and Tim.

Tim puts the goggles on. He climbs into the rear of the car as the large lenses illuminate and focus on Grant and Malcolm's car, which he sees in a bright fluorescent green. "Wow, cool, night-vision!"

The goat bleats on and on. Tim hears a faint, dull thud. Then another. He pulls off the goggles, looks worried, reaches and puts his hand on Lex's shoulder, "Did you feel that?"

He moves forward, staring at two plastic cups of water that sit in the dashboard recess. The water is moving in slow, rhythmic circles – the hint of a faint vibration. It stops. Then starts again. Boom, boom, boom – getting slightly louder.

Gennaro is now aware of the vibration and of the dull thud, like someone, or something is walking with slow, deliberate heavy footsteps, "Maybe it's the power trying to come back on." He convinces no-one, including himself.

Tim puts the night-vision goggles back on and looks out towards the tethered goat. Only the goat is no longer there, only the chain, swinging from the stake. "Where's the goat?" Lex asks Tim as a loud bang against the sunroof startles them all. It's the torn-off leg of the goat.

They all shrink back in fear, Tim looks out through the goggles again, seeing a huge claw grip the cables of the once electrified fence. A roar and a twenty-five foot tyrannosaurus rex comes into view.

Gennaro frantically pushes open the door and runs rapidly past Grant and Malcolm's car into an outdoor restroom, shuts the door and sits on the loo, cowering. Lex is screaming, she cannot believe Gennaro has left them stranded and alone.

Grant and Malcolm, totally oblivious to what's just happened, watch puzzled. "Where does he think he's going?" wonders Grant.

Malcolm shrugs, "When you gotta go, you gotta go." They turn back to the front just as the fence begins to fall, cables snapping and flying off, posts falling. The T-rex walks into the road, stopping between the two vehicles.

Lex is still fearful as the brachiosaur grazes.

> The noise causes the animal to move it's massive head, huge teeth exposed, down to the level of the car. A large, yellow eye stares at the two terrified children.

It begins to prowl, very slowly. Looking at one car and then the other. Malcolm mutters something about hating being right all the time. The massive head looks down at Grant and Malcolm.

Grant whispers, fear in his voice, "Don't move, his vision's based on movement." The snout comes down and begins to slowly, almost gently bang against the car.

A light shines brightly from the car. Lex has found a flashlight, it's pointing at the other car – and the T-rex. It turns and begins to move.

"Turn the light off, turn the light off," Grant, barely able to speak wills Lex to turn it off. The huge, dangerous dinosaur moves slowly, menacingly towards the light as Tim screams at Lex to turn the light off, the T-rex stops momentarily. Tim pulls the door, left open by Gennaro, shut. The noise causes the animal to move it's massive head, huge teeth exposed, down to the level of the car. A large, yellow eye stares at the two terrified children.

They cover their ears as the beast roars, it's horrifying mouth wide open – the jaws of death. The beast presses it's massive snout against the car and begins to rock it as the children scream. Tim scrambles alongside Lex shouting for her to turn the flashlight off as the beam shines up through the sunroof.

The Plexiglas sunroof falls down as the T-rex shoves as much as it can of it's huge head into the car with a sickening roar. The children are trapped beneath the Plexiglas, screaming in sheer terror, as the dinosaur's jaw bangs against it. It's trying to eat them.

Grant and Malcolm watch, rooted to the spot, the total horror taking place before them.

Frustrated the T-rex once again decides to turn the car over. It's head bangs against the side and the car goes over on to its roof. The kids scream helplessly as they are thrown about. The animal is now ripping the car to shreds, biting off the first thing that it's mouth finds on the under-carriage. It puts its front legs up on the overturned car and the car begins to sink into the ground. The mud comes in through the open windows and the car begins to fill up. Tim and Lex are in danger of drowning in mud.

Still hesitant.

Grant feeds the gentle dinosaur.

Gennaro has been listening to the pounding footsteps in abject terror.
Even that did not prepare him for the huge head that explodes into the building.

Grant snaps out of it and reaches into the back of the car, desperately looking for anything that will help. He hurriedly runs out of the car and faces the dinosaur waving a small tube. He calls out to the T-rex and pulls the top of the flare. Bright red flames cause the T-rex to turn and face Grant, swinging his arm in a wide arc. He throws the flare, the dinosaur takes off after it. Malcolm appears waving another flare and the dinosaur takes off after him. Grant is screaming for Malcolm to get rid of the flare as Malcolm heads towards the outdoor restroom. He throws the flare to one side as a bolt of lightning lights up the restroom. The animal brushes by Malcolm, knocking him down and unconscious.

Gennaro has been listening to the pounding footsteps in abject terror. Even that did not prepare him for the huge head that explodes into the building. The walls collapse like a house of cards, Gennaro is sat in the open. The T-rex eyes him with interest, just for a moment, then the jaws come swiftly down and Gennaro is suddenly in the air with only his legs protruding from the massive jaws as the beast begins to shake it's head back and forth.

Grant reaches into the car and retrieves a mud-covered Lex by dragging her out, telling Tim, trapped by a seat, that he'll get him out next. As he begins to do so, Lex lets out a piercing scream. The T-rex is back and stood only a few yards in front of them. Grant leaps to his feet, grabs Lex and covers her mouth with his hand, telling her, "Don't move. He can't see us if we don't move!"

The T-rex's long neck reaches out and the massive head looms down – and down. The jaws are right in front of Grant's face. Less than six inches away. The head nods slightly and Grant's safari hat is knocked off, they remain still, very still.

Suddenly the huge head moves with surprising quickness and bangs against the front of the upturned car spinning it round in the mud. Lex and Grant seem to be moved round with it like in some bizarre children's chasing game. Tim screams as he lies flat inside against the upturned

> "So the only way to find them is to search the computer's lines of code one by one."
>
> "How many lines of code are there?"
>
> "About two million," comes the sombre reply.

Hammond wonders on the fate of his grandchildren.

roof. The car continues to move, but now it's being shoved towards a barrier. A barrier that has a sixty foot drop behind it.

Grant and Lex are between the moving car and the barrier about to be crushed, they leap on top of the barrier. Grant almost falls from the three foot wide wall but manages to get his balance back. The T-rex continues crashing it's huge head against the car, trying to tip it over the barrier. Grant pulls Lex onto his back, grabs one of the hanging steel fence cables and climbs down a dozen feet. They look up and see the car about to be pushed over, they're right in its path. Lex, clinging on for dear life, is now inadvertently choking the struggling Grant. More of the car comes into view. Grant swings the cable and, using his feet against the wall, tries desperately to reach another hanging cable. The car begins to topple, Grant swings yet again. The car crashes down, Grant and Ellie swing away on the second cable. The car has landed on the top of a tree. The T-rex looks down, roars and walks away as if to say there's no fun anymore.

In the control room it's now apparent that Dennis Nedry had disappeared. Ray Arnold, cigarette burning brightly, has an audience of Hammond, Muldoon and Ellie as he points to Nedry's computer screen which is a mass of commands, all of them incomprehensible, "Keycheck space minus O, Keychecks off, safety space minus O. He's turning the safety systems off. He doesn't want anybody to see what he's about to do. Now, look at this next entry, it's the kicker. 'White, rabbit, object.' Whatever it did, it did it all. But with the keychecks off, the computer didn't file the keystrokes. So the only way to find them is to search the computer's lines of code one by one."

"How many lines of code are there?" Ellie asks Arnold.

"About two million," comes the sombre reply. There is a slight, stunned silence.

Hammond, ashen-faced, turns to Muldoon and asks him if he'll take a gas jeep and get his grandchildren. Ellie volunteers to go with him and they leave. Arnold turns to Hammond and calls his name. Hammond just stares into space.

Tension mounts as Jurassic Park is still off-line.

"Malcolm was right — life has found a way!"

Nedry turns around and sees the dilophosaur.
It's only about four feet high, harmless looking, almost like a large cuddly toy.

Arnold calls again and Hammond turns, "John, I can't get Jurassic Park back on line without Dennis Nedry."

Dennis Nedry's jeep roars through the mud. He shakes his head, he should have been at the dock long ago. He looks out of the side window into the rain, hoping for an indication of where he is, and looks back through the windscreen straight at a barrier. He brakes, skids and goes through the barrier and down an embankment. The jeep is stuck, nose-down and the wheels spin hopelessly as he tries to reverse out. Almost in tears, he gets out of the vehicle as water cascades down the embankment. Nedry cranks a winch from the coil on the front of the jeep. Nedry slips and the water sends him downwards. He lands heavily and loses his spectacles, cursing he blindly looks around for something to attach the winch to. A soft, shrill hooting can be heard from an unknown place. He never sees the sign with the arrow pointing downwards to the 'East Docks.'

He finds a large tree suitable for his purpose, looks at his watch, tells himself he's got time and begins to wrap the winch round the trunk of the tree. The hooting sound is there again, stopping Nedry from his task, it's a lot closer. Nedry turns around and sees the dilophosaur.

It's only about four feet high, harmless looking, almost like a large cuddly toy. It has a crest on top of it's head. Nedry talks to it as though it were a dangerous dog, "Nice boy, nice dinosaur. I thought you were one of your big brothers – you're not so bad. What do you want? You want food? Look at me, I just fell down a hill, I'm soaking wet, I don't have any food. I have nothing on me, go on," Nedry reaches and gets a large twig, he's becoming more confident now – it's not so frightening after all. "Play fetch, play fetch. Look, stick, stick stupid," he waves the stick at the dilophosaur and throws it. The dinosaur doesn't move, only looks at him quizzically. "You don't like your stick? No wonder your extinct. I'm gonna run you over when I come back down." Nedry turns and scrambles back up the embankment to the jeep. He slips near the top and hears the hoot, when he turns the dilophosaur is staring him in the face.

The crest fans out rapidly, the jaws shoot open revealing small but terrifyingly dangerous teeth. It no longer looks cute, the dilophosaur looks positively evil and hisses. An instant later the head snaps forward and a large blob, wet and gooey shoots onto Nedry's chest. He looks surprised, pulls at the goo and rushes to his feet towards the jeep. He turns only for a fraction before the open door. It hits him in the face, the black mess gets into his eyes and it's very painful. He frantically clears the mess away and lunges for the jeep and smashes his head on the door frame, never noticing the shaving cream can pop out of his pocket to be carried away by the water, down the embankment and buried forever in the mud. He recovers and gets in the jeep, relieved. Until he hears the hiss and sees the dilophosaur on the passenger seat. There wasn't a lot left of Dennis Nedry after it finished with him.

Grant and Lex are at the bottom of the barrier that leads up to the park road. Grant washes his face in the water pouring out off a large drain pipe. Up above the Explorer rests in the trees. Grant looks up and shouts Timmy's name. Lex sobs uncontrollably as Grant tells her, "Relax, listen to me, relax. I'm right here, I'm gonna look after you but I'm gonna have to help your brother. Stay right here and wait for me."

Ellie and Muldoon make their way to the power room.

Danger looms.

Fearful for her life, Ellie prepares to sprint.

Lex is hysterical, "He left us, he left us," she still can't believe Gennaro left her and Timmy.

"But that's not what I'm gonna do – okay?" Grant reassures her and she nods her approval and scrambles into the safety of the drain pipe.

Grant, calling Timmy, climbs up the tree towards what's left of the car. The car is pointing downwards – as if the tree were the road. He finds the frightened, huddled boy still inside, shocked but relatively unhurt. "I threw up," he whimpers.

"That's okay. Give me your hand," Grant softy replies as he reaches for Timmy, wary that the car could fall under the extra weight. Timmy doesn't move. "I won't tell anybody you threw up. Just give me your hand, okay?" They both reach for each other. As Grant leans on the steering wheel to get closer, the wheels turn, branches begin to creak and snap.

Slowly, very slowly they climb out of the car. Timmy is now frightened about the climb down as they come to a rest, the car hovering precariously above them. Grant explains it's just like climbing down from a tree house, Timmy tells him he's never had a tree house, just before the car shifts downwards another couple of feet. They look up at it, the branches creak again. "Go!" Grant and Timmy move down the tree with surprising speed, the car follows them before thick

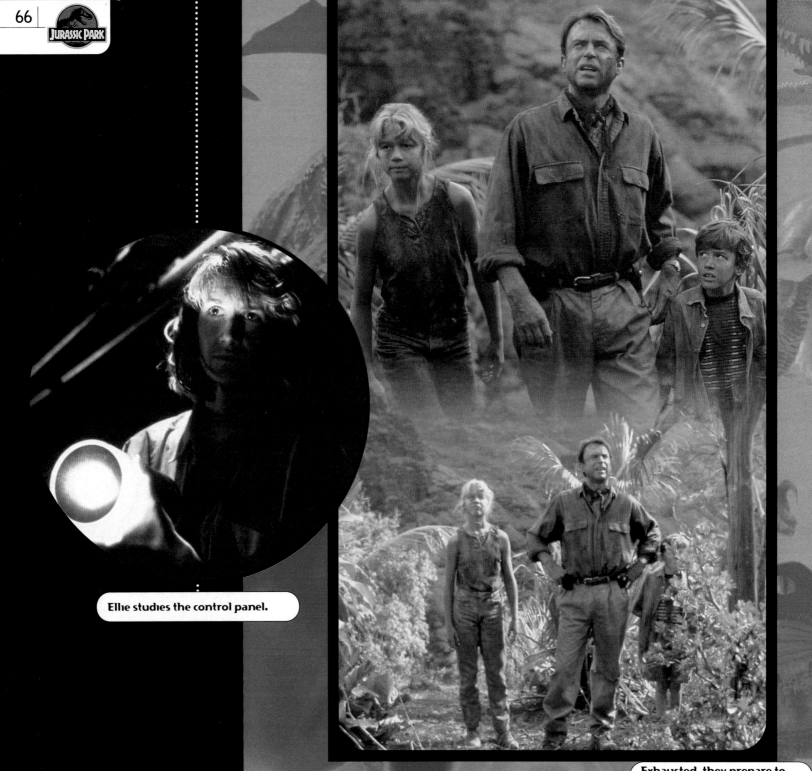

Ellie studies the control panel.

Exhausted, they prepare to climb the electric fence.

They find Malcolm, his leg badly damaged, laying in the road, just as he's coming round, "Remind me to thank John for a lovely weekend," he whispers.

branches stop its fall, momentarily. They look up again, the car is only a few feet from them and ready to fall as the branches weaken. "Go! Go! Go!" and they race down the tree again, the car races after them spreading and breaking branches as it rapidly descends. They leap from the tree about six feet from the ground. A few feet behind them the car nose-dives into the earth. They look back and see the car about to topple towards them. Grant yells and they race forward, rolling into a ball as the car crashes down on top of them, the undercarriage on top. They're saved by the supports holding what's left of the roof, hitting the ground and keeping the rest of the car from crushing them.

"Well, we're back in the car again," Timmy gasps.

"Well at least you're out of the tree," Grant wearily replies.

Muldoon and Ellie's gas powered jeep screams to a halt as they find the remaining Explorer. They frantically shine their flashlights, searching for the second car and any signs of life.

They find Malcolm, his leg badly damaged, laying in the road, just as he's coming round, "Remind me to thank John for a lovely weekend," he whispers. The roar of a T-rex somewhere in the night echoes around them. They manage to get Malcolm into the jeep. Ellie shines her flashlight over the barrier and shouts that she's found the other car. Muldoon and Ellie scramble down and investigate the empty, broken vehicle. Ellie shines her light on two sets of footprints moving away from the car.

Malcolm too is looking at footprints. The large print of the T-rex, half filled with rainwater, the water circling as something very large, and very loud appears to be approaching. Ellie and Muldoon come back from the embankment, running, aware of the noise. Malcolm yells for them to move it and they scramble alongside him. The engine bursts to life just as the T-rex bursts into view.

The night rings with their screams of terror as the dinosaur closes in on them. Closer and closer. It's huge head, now only a few feet away, slowly comes down preparing to strike. Ellie

Grant makes light of the impending danger.

Ellie prepares to put Jurassic Park back on-line.

> "I hate trees," Timmy, with good reason, mutters.
> "They don't bother me," Lex states.
> "You weren't in the last one," Timmy has the final word on tree-climbing.

screams as a half-fallen tree looms up, blocking the road. They all duck as the jeep speeds under the trunk with inches to spare. The T-rex crashes into the tree and right through it, it's head swinging into the side of the jeep almost knocking it off the road as it makes one last, desperate lunge. But the jeep's pulling away now as Muldoon guns it for all it's worth, the T-rex slows down and almost seems to shrug as it's prey fades into the distance.

Grant, Tim and Lex slowly move through Jurassic Park, tired and still frightened. A roar in the distance gives them no reassurance. Grant leads them to the base of a huge, twisted tree as another roar pierces the night air. They need a place of safety and to rest – they start to climb the tree.

"I hate trees," Timmy, with good reason, mutters.

"They don't bother me," Lex states.

"You weren't in the last one," Timmy has the final word on tree-climbing.

They come to rest high up on thick branches. Lex and Tim nestle besides Grant, who doesn't look as uncomfortable with this situation as he would have done earlier in the day. It's now a beautiful, calm night and the moonlit view over the park is spectacular. In the distance they can see the long necks of a herd of brontosaurs. Strange, almost musical, sounds ring out in the night.

"They're singing!" Grant exclaims. He stands cupping his hands and tries to imitate the sounds. Two sauropod heads on the end of long necks rise up close to the tree.

"Don't get the monsters over here!" Lex, still frightened.

"They're not monsters, Lex. They're just animals – these are herbivores," Grant gently tells her.

"That means they only eat vegetables – but for you I think they'd make an exception," Tim teases.

"Well I hate the other kind," Lex points out.

"They just do what they do," Grant answers.

The children nestle closer to him than before, his arms around them. Grant winces and pulls something out of his back pocket. It's the velociraptor claw he showed to the kid in Montana what seemed an eternity ago – it was only yesterday. He looks at it thinking how excited he was to find such things – now he's in a land of living dinosaurs.

"What are you and Ellie gonna do now if you don't have to dig up dinosaur bones any more?" Lex seems to read his thoughts.

"I guess I'll just have to evolve too," Grant lets the claw fall from his hand.

"What do you call a blind dinosaur?" Tim yawns, Grant doesn't know. "A Do-you-think-he-saurus. What do you call a blind dinosaur's dog?" Grant shakes his head. "A Do-you-think-he-saurus Rex." Grant laughs and pulls the kids closer to him.

"What if the dinosaurs come while we're all asleep," Lex asks.

"I'll stay awake," Grant says.

"All night?" Lex is sceptical.

"All night," Grant looks at the children as they close their eyes.

Ellie walks through the darkened restaurant towards the lonely and sad figure of John Hammond, sitting at a table toying with a dish of melting ice-cream. She tells him that Malcolm is going to be okay, they've given him a shot of morphine.

Hammond looks at her, his eyes filling up "They'll be fine. Who better to get the children through Jurassic Park than a dinosaur expert?"

He reminisces with fondness about his first attraction, a flea circus in Petticoat Lane. About the carousel and the seesaw and the trapeze. And how people would swear they could see the clown flees and the highwire fleas.

"With this place, I just wanted to give them something real, something that wasn't an illusion, something they could see and touch – an idea that's not devoid of merit."

"You can't think your way out of this one, John. You have to feel it," Ellie tells him.

"You're absolutely right. Hiring Nedry was a mistake, that's obvious. We're over-dependent on automation, I see that now. But next time, everything's correctable," he carries on as Ellie tries to interrupt, "Creation is an act of sheer will. Next time it will be flawless."

Ellie is getting a little angry "John, you're still trying to build onto your Flea Circus. It's all an illusion."

"When we have control again …"

DANGER 10,000 VOLTS

ace again Tim has a problem with heights.

DANGER
10,000
VOLTS

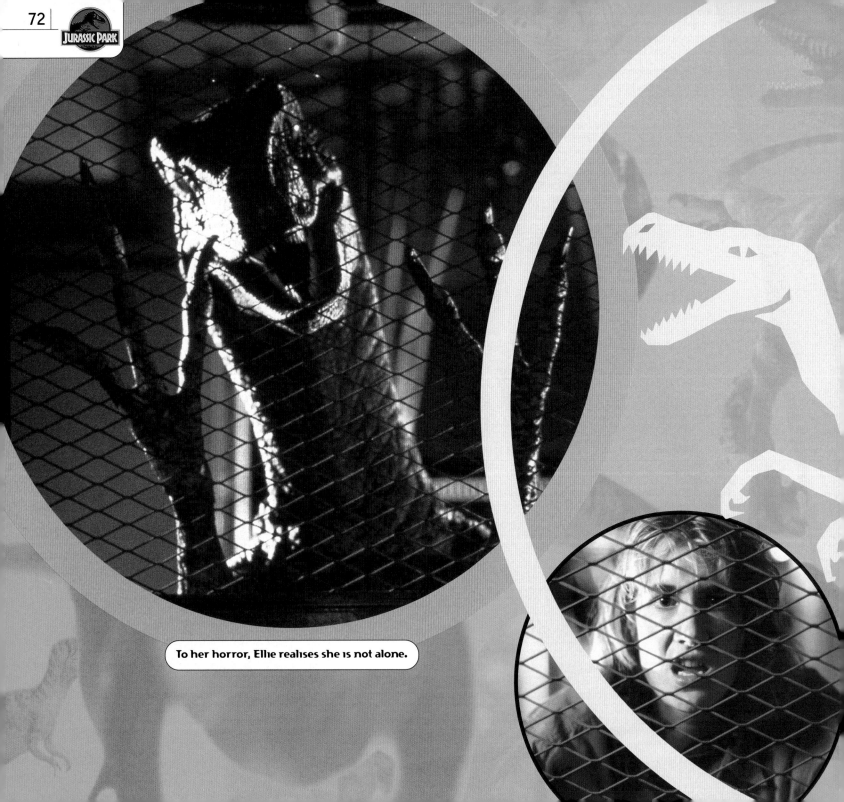

To her horror, Ellie realises she is not alone.

> "John, you're still trying to build onto your Flea Circus. It's all an illusion."
>
> "When we have control again ..."
>
> "You never had control! That's the illusion."

"You never had control! That's the illusion. I was overwhelmed by the power of this place but I made a mistake, too. I didn't have enough respect for that power and it's out now. The only thing that matters now are the people we love. Alan, Lex and Tim. John, they're out there and people are dying," Ellie, emotionally drained, dips a spoon into the ice-cream, tastes and smiles.

"Spared no expense," Hammond says as he stares into her eyes.

It's a beautiful morning in Jurassic Park as the sun comes up. Grant, Lex and Tim, still huddled together in the tree, slowly begin to awake. A large shadow falls over them – the massive head of a brachiosaur. It begins to eat the branches and leaves right next to them. Lex is once again horrified.

"It's okay! It's okay! It's a brachiosaur!" Grant tells the frightened Lex as she cowers away.

"Veggiesaurus, Lex, veggiesaurus!" Tim playfully tells her, his eyes staring with wonder. Grant pulls off some branches and feeds the huge animal. Tim strokes it's head and when Grant tells Lex to think of it as a huge cow, even she nervously goes to pat it. Just as it sneezes right into her face.

"God bless you!" Tim calls after the departing animal. Lex is not impressed.

They climb down from the tree and Lex stomps to the front, still annoyed with the brachiosaur.

"Oh great. Now she'll never try anything!" Tim moans, "She'll just sit in her room and never come out and play with her computer ..."

"I'm a hacker!" Lex yells back at him.

"That's what I said, Nerd!"

"I'm not a computer nerd! I prefer to be called a hacker!"

Grant stops and stares at the ground and the white fragments. He crouches down, picks up one of the pieces and studies it. The children gather round, "Do you know what this is? It's an egg, a dinosaur egg – the dinosaur's are breeding."

Tim looks mystified "But my grandpa said all the dinosaurs were girls!"

> **"Malcolm was right!" He points to tiny footprints leading away from the eggs, "Life found a way!"**

Grant's eyes open wider with realisation, "Amphibian DNA! On the tour, the film said they used frog DNA to fill in the gene sequence gaps. They mutated the dinosaur's genetic code and blended it with that of the frogs. Now some West African frogs have been known to spontaneously change sex from male to female in a single sex environment. Malcolm was right!" He points to tiny footprints leading away from the eggs, "Life found a way!"

Ray Arnold, tired and weary sits once again at his terminal. Ellie, Muldoon and the recovering Malcolm look on as Arnold speaks to Hammond, "No, no, no. That's crazy. You're out of your mind – he's out of his mind."

"Now wait a minute," asks Ellie "What exactly would this mean?"

Hammond answers, "We're talking about a calculated risk, my dear, which is about the only option left to us. We will never find the command that Nedry used, he covered his tracks far too well and I think it's obvious now that he's not coming back. Shutting down the entire system …"

"You can get somebody else because I won't do it," Arnold interrupts.

Hammond continues, "Shutting down the system is the only way to wipe out everything that he did. Now, as I understand it, all the systems will then come back on their original start-up mode. Correct?"

"Theoretically, yes, but we've never shut down the entire system before. It may not come back on at all," Arnold is not impressed.

"Would we get the phones back?" Ellie asks Arnold.

"Yeah, again, in theory," Arnold replies, taking a long pull on his cigarette.

Muldoon studies for a moment, "What about the lysine contingency? We could put that into effect."

"What's that?" Ellie asks hopefully.

"That is absolutely out of the question," Hammond states firmly.

Muldoon senses he's being watched.

JURASSIC PARK

"Clever girl ..."

Relief — momentarily, for Ellie ...

... and Tim.

> **"Out in the maintenance shed. Other end of the compound. Three minutes and I'll have power back on in the entire park," Arnold tells them all with confidence.**

"It was intended to prevent the spread of the animals just in case they ever got off the island, but we could use it now. Dr. Wu inserted a gene that makes a single faulty enzyme in protein metabolism. The animals can't manufacture the amino acid lysine. Unless they're constantly supplied with lysine by us, they'll go into a coma and die," Arnold explains.

Hammond turns and walks up to Arnold, "People are dying. Will you please shut down the system!"

Ray Arnold reluctantly walks over to a red metal box situated on the wall. He takes a key from his belt unlocks the door and opens it. He flips off the first three switches as terminals go off all over the control room. His hand hesitates over the fourth one.

"Hold onto your butts," he knocks it down and everything is plunged into darkness. Muldoon's flashlight snaps on.

Moments later Arnold is attracted by a faint, continuous bleeping sound. He walks over to a monitor where 'System Ready' flashes in the bottom left hand corner. "It's okay! Look, see that. It's on. It worked!"

They all rush over to the terminal except for the injured Malcolm, who asks, "Wait a minute, what do you mean it worked? Everything's still off!"

"The shutdown must have tripped the circuit breakers. All we have to do is just turn them back on, reboot a few systems in here – phones, security doors, half a dozen others – but it worked! System's ready!" Arnold is triumphant.

"Where are the breakers?" Muldoon asks Arnold.

"Out in the maintenance shed. Other end of the compound. Three minutes and I'll have power back on in the entire park," Arnold tells them all with confidence.

"Now, just to be safe, I want everybody in the emergency bunker until Mr. Arnold returns and the whole system's up and running again," Hammond insists.

Grant, Tim and Lex head through the open park grounds towards the top of a rise, hot and tired. Grant is confident that they're not too far from the Visitor's Centre. A low rumble catches

A joyous Ellie and Grant find each other.

their attention and they look down from the rise.

There are dozens of stampeding dinosaurs running across their view. They are gallimimus by name, an ostrich-like creature, approximately 10 or 12 foot tall. Tim correctly names them and Lex queries if they're meat eaters.

Grant stares at the beauty of the sight as they swing round, "They're beautiful. And the direction changes – just like a flock of birds evading a predator."

Tim nervously backs away, "They're flocking this way!" He and Lex take off, Grant running after them as the animals thunder over the rise.

They run as fast as they can go. Some of the animals overtake them, swerving to avoid a collision. The others are pounding on behind them. A large, old tree trunk lays leafless on the ground and the three race towards it, leaping over and shielding themselves against the far side as some of the animals take the obstacle easily in their stride.

The herd has passed on and all three rise, just in time to see what they were running from. The huge T-rex lunges out from the trees at the side of the meadow ripping one of it's victims to pieces in seconds. They stare at the feeding T-rex until Lex decides it's time for them to move on, carefully.

Inside the bunker, patience is running out as they wait for the power to return. Hammond, still hopeful that Jurassic Park will succeed, explains to Muldoon, Malcolm and Ellie that Disneyland had problems when it first opened. Malcolm reminds him that if the 'Pirates of the Caribbean' break down the pirates don't devour the tourists. Ellie finally has enough and declares that she's going to get the power back on. Muldoon quickly volunteers to go with her.

Muldoon opens a steel cabinet and removes a high-powered shotgun as Hammond opens a set of blueprints. They agree Hammond will direct them through the large maintenance shed via walkie-talkie – once they get there.

Muldoon and Ellie step cautiously out of the bunker. The compound is silent and empty and has the unexplainable smell of danger. They move quicker, but not for long. The fence round the raptor pen is badly damaged, bent and twisted metal high above. Muldoon curses, "The shutdown turned off all the fences. Damn it! Even Nedry knew better than to mess with the raptor fence!"

He leads Ellie into the jungle foliage and towards the maintenance shed. They are very, very cautious now, sensing something. Ellie spots the shed and tells Muldoon they can make it if they run.

Tim hides, in fear for his life.

Ellie spots the shed and tells Muldoon they can make it if they run.
"No. We can't," Muldoon answers grimly, "because we're being hunted. From the bushes. Straight ahead."

"No. We can't," Muldoon answers grimly, "because we're being hunted. From the bushes. Straight ahead. It's all right," he tells Ellie as he stares, gripping his gun, into the bushes. "Run, towards the shed – I've got her! Run! Now!" Muldoon stays put.

Ellie tears through the foliage at breakneck speed and breathlessly reaches the maintenance shed. She yanks open the door and calls Hammond on the walkie-talkie to let him know she made it. She descends the stairs shining the flashlight and calling in vain for Ray Arnold, as Hammond directs her towards the power switch.

At that very moment, Grant, Tim and Lex, exhausted, have finally made it to the electrical fence surrounding the main compound. A sign tells them of the danger and the 10,000 volts that await anyone, or anything, that touches the fence. Grant glances up at the dead warning lights and throws a stick against the fence. The children watch anxiously as he stretches his hands out, announcing that he believes the power to be off. He grips the fence with both hands and screams. The children, horrified, scream and Grant laughs. He turns to them with a wide grin on his face. Tim likes the joke, Lex is not amused.

Grant strains, hoping to make a hole big enough in the fence. An all too familiar roar sounds in the far distance and all three hurriedly start the steep climb.

Hammond has directed Ellie into a dead end. He studies the blueprint and informs Ellie he's given her the wrong turn. Frustrated, Malcolm grabs the walkie-talkie from him and takes over as Hammond blusters and protests.

"Look above you – there should be a large bundle of cable and white PVC tubing all leading in the same direction! Just follow that!" Malcolm tells Ellie, who shines her flashlight upwards and follows the trail to the power switch.

The hunt is on.

As Grant jumps down from the fence a grinding warning noise comes from above. He looks up at the flashing warning lights. The children are still on the fence, only now they're panicking.

The raptor senses movement ...

Grant, Tim and Lex are near the top of the fence. Timmy and Lex banter about who's gonna get over the other side first. Grant reminds them that it's not a race.

Ellie's walking faster now, more confident. She reports back that a sign says 'High Voltage,' opens the door and steps inside.

They're at the top of the fence now, getting ready to climb over and down. Grant reminds them to watch their footing – and take their time.

Hammond, back now in control, tells Ellie "You can't throw the main switch by hand, you have to pump up the primer handle to give you a charge. It's large, flat and grey ..."

"Here we go, okay!" Ellie has found it and is now pumping the handle up and down. She steps back as an indicator clicks over to 'Charged.' She keeps Hammond up to date.

"Good! Under the words 'contact position' there's a round green button that says 'push to close.' Push it!" Hammond gives Ellie the final instruction. She looks on the control panel, finds the button and presses it. On the panel lights start to come on.

As Grant jumps down from the fence a grinding warning noise comes from above. He looks up at the flashing warning lights. The children are still on the fence, only now they're panicking.

The buttons on the control panel have all come to life now. Hammond tells Ellie that they control individual areas of the park. He tells her to switch them all on. There are twelve buttons set out in the control panel vertically. Ellie starts from the top – the last one reads 'Perimeter Fences.'

Lex has got off the fence. Tim is still on the fence. He doesn't appear to have moved.

A hand drops onto her shoulder.
She breathes a sigh of relief, "Oh Mr. Arnold,"
and clasps the arm. Only there's nothing
attached to the arm except the hand.

He looks like an animal trapped in a pair of bright headlights. Grant and Lex scream at him to come down as the warning lights flash faster and faster.

Ellie's pressing the buttons as fast as she can.

Grant yells at him to come down. Count to three. Tim doesn't move. Grant moves to climb the fence to get him down. Lex, with surprising strength, pulls him back. Tim pulls himself together, decides to count to three and begins the count.

Ellie is three buttons from the bottom of the strip.

"One, two ..." Timmy flies off as the power bites into the fence. He's thrown backwards straight towards Grant who tries to catch him, they both hit the ground.
Grant looks at the fallen boy and then at Lex, "He's not breathing."

Ellie clasps her hands together and does a dance of joy. She's done it, she's got the power on. The raptors head bursts through the pipes at the side of her. It roars, she screams and turns, stumbling towards the mesh door. She gets through, tries to close the door shut as she is knocked backwards as the raptor crashes into it. She kicks her feet out and the door slams shut against the raptor. She's knocked backwards by the sheer force. A hand drops onto her shoulder.

She breathes a sigh of relief, "Oh Mr. Arnold," and clasps the arm. Only there's nothing attached to the arm except the hand. Ellie drops the bloody stump to the floor as she steps backwards in sheer terror. The raptor's head forces it's way through the mesh, inches from the screaming Ellie.

She's limping badly as she bolts up the metal stairway. The raptor's disengaged itself from the mesh gate and is in hot pursuit. She slams the heavy metal shed door shut and falls to the ground in tears.

... they know the children are close.

With deadly precision the evil duo move in for the kill.

Robert Muldoon cautiously stalks his prey. He sees it now. Right in front of him. He takes his time, primes the gun and takes aim. It's the second raptor that kills him. It comes out of the foliage from his left side. He only had time to whisper "clever girl," and turn his gun before it tore him to pieces.

At the perimeter fence Grant is trying desperately to revive Tim. Pounding on his chest and breathing air into his mouth. A sobbing Lex can only watch. Timmy splutters and comes to life. Grant hugs the kid and strokes his head. Lex now cries tears of joy.

They walk into the empty restaurant, Grant carrying Tim. Grant sits the boy down at a table and tells the children that he needs to find the others, and to get Tim seen to by a doctor. Grant asks Lex to look after Tim.

He looks at the boy once more. "Your hair's all standing up," Grant rearranges Tim's hair and the two smile at each other, "Big Tim, the human piece of toast." Grant promises to be right back and goes to search for the others.

Tim gets up and hobbles towards a table where a large selection of goodies are temptingly laid out, Lex follows, heading for the cakes and Jell-o.

Outside of the Visitors Centre Grant calls Ellie's name. She struggles into view. Limping badly she runs as fast as she can towards him and into his arms.

A translucent mural, depicting dinosaurs, is the backdrop for Tim and Lex as they begin to eat. Their ordeal now over, the kids are ravenous. They scoop food into their mouths and grin at each other.

Suddenly they stop grinning as Lex's Jell-o begins to quiver in her hand. On the dinosaur mural behind them a silhouette slowly appears. The children stare in disbelief. They move, arm in arm, as fast as they can towards the kitchen before the raptor can see them. Lex closes the door behind them – there's no lock, but she makes sure the handle snaps into position.

They hide at the far end of the aisle, behind a long counter. The small round window in the kitchen door steams up as the raptor snorts against it, then a yellow eye comes into view. The children duck down quickly, but not quick enough.

> **"Just the two raptors, right? You sure the third one's contained?"**
> **"Yes — unless they figure out how to open doors."**

In the bunker, as Hammond and Malcolm look on, Grant primes the heavy duty gun and turns towards Ellie. "Just the two raptors, right? You sure the third one's contained?"

"Yes – unless they figure out how to open doors," Ellie replies.

The kitchen door handle begins to turn. Lex and Tim cannot believe what they are seeing. The raptor's head pushes the door open and it enters the room.

"Timmy, what is it?" Lex whispers.

"It's a velociraptor," Timmy whispers back.

"It's inside," Lex trembles with fear.

The raptor lifts it's head high and lets out a series of sickening barks causing the children to cover their ears and shake in sheer terror. Suddenly the raptor is joined by another one. They begin to prowl separately down two of the three aisles of long stainless steel counters and work surfaces. The kids crawl up the empty aisle in the opposite direction, very slowly and very quietly. A snorting raptor's head shoots over, looking, but not seeing anything. A long tail swings and pots and pans go flying and clatter on top of them causing them to make a dash and hide for a moment at the end of one of the aisles, just as the raptors head shoots through the open cabinet to find nothing there.

Tim, falling behind Lex, brushes against some hanging utensils and they clatter to the floor. The raptors heads spring up, alert and sniffing. They move in on Tim.

One of the raptors leaps on top of the counter and joins the other in the search for Tim. Lex at the far end of the aisle silently urges Tim to follow her. He seems frozen as the raptors get closer and closer. A huge head begins to turn the corner where Tim is hiding when a loud tapping noise causes the head to shoot inquisitively up. Lex is feverishly banging a large spoon on the kitchen floor. The raptors turn their attention to Lex.

Lex climbs into a small steel cabinet behind her, confident the raptors won't find her. Only one problem, she can't get the sliding door to shut. She frantically pulls and struggles with the door as one of the raptors charges towards her, picking up speed as it moves for the kill.

Lex and Tim, now in the control room are unaware that danger is still close at hand.

The door still won't shut. The raptor hurls itself at Lex and crashes headlong into her reflection in the steel cabinet opposite.

Tim sees Lex escape from the semi-conscious raptor and decides it's time to make a move. He looks around as much as he dares and runs, almost on one leg, down the aisle towards the walk-in freezer. He's only gone about three paces when the other raptor spots him and leaps over the counter and pursues the crippled Tim down the aisle, gaining ground every second. Thumping along, the raptor's just about to make his kill when Timmy reaches the walk-in freezer and pulls the door open and falls inside. The floor is icy and slippy and he can't get up to close the door. The raptor comes hurtling in and slips right past him. Timmy's feet slide on the floor as he struggles alongside the downed raptor, it's a race to see who can get up first. Timmy drags himself up a fraction before the raptor and makes it out of the freezer as the raptor hurtles after him. It's head gets trapped in the door as Timmy tries to close it. Lex, screaming, comes running along with outstretched arms and between them they force the door closed as the raptor retreats. They drop the pin and the freezer door is securely locked.

They move towards the restaurant through the kitchen, at the far end the other raptor snorts and roars. They run straight into the arms of Grant and Ellie. Lex points to the kitchen and breathlessly tells them that the raptor's in there. They back away, Grant ready with the gun, to the control room.

They rush through the door, Lex asks if they can call for help as Ellie runs over to a terminal, explaining that they have to reboot the system first. Grant looks at the door and realises it won't lock because the locks are controlled by the system. That's when the raptor's head came into view outside the door and started to force it's way in, knocking Grant back and sending the gun flying. Grant pushes against the door as Ellie comes to help him. Grant screams for her to reboot the system, she screams back that he can't hold the door by himself. Ellie tries to hook the strap of the gun with her boot but she can't quite reach it, if she moves away any further from the door, the raptor's going to get in.

Lex sits at the terminal, "It's a Unix system – I know this." She's into it immediately, exploring her way through the screen graphics, trying to find the right file.

They can't hold it much longer, claws come round the door. They push harder and the claws disappear. Then the door moves

In the control room, Grant battles with an unwelcome visitor.

They look on as the raptors meet their match.

"The children are fine, call the mainland, tell them to send the damn helicopters," Grant tells Hammond as Ellie, Lex and Tim grin behind him. Grant drops the phone as the raptor crashes against the glass panelled wall.

again and the claws come into view again. One last push, the claws go back and the locks snap shut.

Lex has cracked the system. Panting, Ellie and Grant join the children. Grant asks what works and a proud Lex tells him "Phones, security systems, you name it – we got it." Grant grabs a phone and calls Hammond.

Hammond and Malcolm look up, shocked at the sound of the ringing phone. Hammond picks up the receiver, "Grant?"

"Mr. Hammond, the phones are working."

"Are the children all right?"

"The children are fine, call the mainland, tell them to send the damn helicopters," Grant tells Hammond as Ellie, Lex and Tim grin behind him.

Grant drops the phone as the raptor crashes against the glass panelled wall. A stricken Hammond can hear gunshots being fired and screams through the receiver.

Grant grabs a builder's ladder and they all scramble up through a ceiling panel and into the ceiling crawl space as the raptor explodes into the control room, shattering glass everywhere. It jumps on to the terminal tables as the ladder is kicked away.

They crawl along the flimsy panels. The raptor looks up curiously as the grilled panels bend under the weight. Lex shoots up as the raptor's head smashes upwards, lifting the panel she's crawling on. Grant violently kicks it in the face and it falls backwards to the floor. And so does Lex. She grabs hold of the edge of the opening and sways from the ceiling as the raptor lies on it's back. It flips to it's feet and roars upwards, jaws open. Grant, using all his strength jerks Lex back up into the ceiling as the raptor's jaws snap shut on nothing but air.

They move to the air duct as fast as they can. Grant finds a large metal grate and heaves it up. They're above the Visitor's Centre lobby. Directly below them is the scaffolding around the dinosaur skeletons. They climb from the duct and onto the nearest platform of the scaffolding. Just as the raptor roars and appears on the balcony opposite them.

It's too far to jump so Lex, Tim and Ellie follow Grant onto the skeleton of the huge brachiosaur. And so does the raptor. The skeleton begins to disintegrate.

Ellie swings helplessly around in circles on the suspended tail-bone. Lex similarly on a part of the shattered neck. Grant lowers Tim to the ground from the massive body just as the ceiling supports holding the cables and the dinosaur skeleton up begin to give way. Lex gets dumped down safely and upright astride the bones she has clung onto. Ellie falls a little harder, and a small shower of bones and plaster fall around her. Tim looks up to see Grant and a large part of the skeleton hurtling towards him. Grant falls one way and the skeleton lands on top of Tim, sharp, lethal bones landing either side of him, just like a small cage.

Ellie looks up, from behind a hanging white builder's sheet she sees a shadow. Then a head peers out, it's the other raptor. The fallen raptor has now got to it's feet. They both approach, from opposite sides. The four humans, huddled together, have nowhere left to run. The first snarling raptor lunges forward for the kill.

The massive jaws catch the raptor in mid-air and the screaming animal is lifted up and up into the air. The massive tyrannosaurus rex whips its head from side to side and throws the dead raptor to the ground. Grant, Ellie, Lex and Tim look at the T-rex, who has saved them from certain death, in amazement. The other raptor, no longer interested in the humans, screams and hurls itself into the air and bites deep into the Rex's side where it hangs on. The T-rex snaps it's jaws backwards as it tries to get the raptor off.

They see their chance to escape and run from the lobby and outside. Hammond and Malcolm squeal to a halt in their jeep. They quickly get in and Grant looks directly at Hammond, "Mr. Hammond, after careful consideration, I've decided not to endorse your park."

"So have I." John Hammond drives away.

The T-rex stomps downwards and partially dislodges the raptor, just enough to whip his head round and get the animal between it's teeth and then throw it out of its mouth into the remains of the hanging Tyrannosaurus Rex skeleton. As the skeleton collapses the T-rex rears it's head triumphantly as a banner falls downwards around it. The banner states 'When Dinosaurs Ruled The Earth.'

Before they climb wearily, but gratefully into the helicopter, Hammond takes one last, sad look at his dream park before Grant helps him along to the helicopter. They quickly take-off, no one speaks, no words are needed right now. Malcolm just stares straight ahead. Grant has both children sat either side of him, sleeping. His arms are draped naturally and protectively around them. Ellie, sitting opposite, smiles at the sight. John Hammond looks at the knob of his walking stick, which is made of amber and has a trapped mosquito inside.

Grant looks outside and sees a flock of graceful birds flying into the sunset. He smiles to himself. 🦖

The ordeal is over.

Dr. Ian Malcolm

Jeff Goldblum

Sarah Harding

Julianne Moore

Roland Tembo

Pete Postlethwaite

Peter Ludlow

Arliss Howard

Dr. John Hammond

Lord Richard Attenborough

Nick Van Owen

Vince Vaughn

Kelly Curtis

Vanessa Lee Chester

Dieter Stark

Peter Stormare

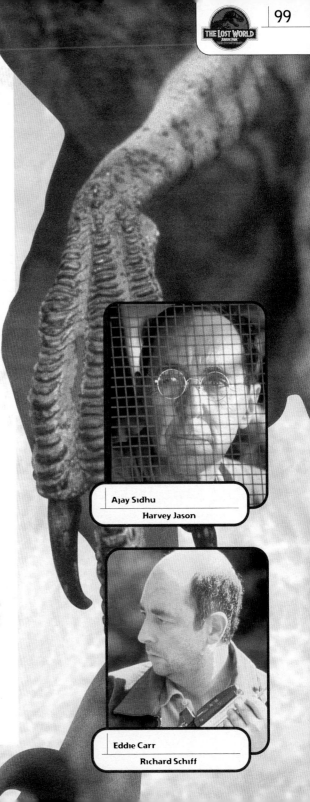

Cast: THE LOST WORLD

Ajay Sidhu
Harvey Jason

Eddie Carr
Richard Schiff

To chain

chain

The Bowman family relax on Isla Sorna.

ISLA SORNA,
87 miles southwest of Isla Nublar.

Isla Sorna, 87 miles southwest of Isla Nublar

Cathy, 7 years old, wanders away down the beach, holding a sandwich in her hand. Her parents are sat around the picnic table which has been set up by the deck hands from the luxury yacht, anchored close by in the tropical lagoon. Mrs Bowman is concerned about Cathy going too far, her husband, reassuring her that there are no snakes on the beach, tells his wife to let the child have some fun for once.

Her parents are no longer visible as she moves round the curve and closer to the jungle foliage. Something is causing the large bush in front of Cathy to move, she gets a little closer, a slightly puzzled look on her face as the bush stops moving and then starts again. A strange creature steps out, about a foot tall, standing on it's hind legs. It's almost lizard-like with dark green skin and brown stripes on it's back. It's head bobs along as it moves towards her. Cathy has no way of knowing that the animal is a compsognathus, a species extinct for millions of years. The puzzled look on Cathy's face has now changed to a huge grin of delight and she offers the compy a bite of her sandwich. She calls for her parents to come and see what she's found. When Cathy turns back to the compy she is suddenly face to face with thirty more, the grin fades as the compy's circle her.

The Bowman's didn't hear their daughter when she first called them but they hear the scream that now breaks the calm silence on the beach. Along with the deck hands they charge along the curving beach. Mrs. Bowman stops dead in her tracks when she gets there, the others rush past as she screams hysterically.

San Diego

Peter Ludlow, late thirties, prematurely balding, addresses the dozen corporate executives sat around the conference table and thanks them all for attending the meeting at such short notice. Ludlow removes a pile of photographs and lets them drop on the table. The board members pass the photographs around, clearly unhappy.

Cathy wanders away unaware of the danger she faces.

The silence is shattered by a terrifying scream.

Old faces greet Malcolm.

Hammond reveals the truth – SITE B.

"These pictures were taken in a hospital in Costa Rica forty-eight hours ago, after a British family on a yacht cruise stumbled onto Site B. The little girl will be fine. Her parents, however, are wealthy, angry and litigious. But that's hardly new to us." Ludlow opens another file and grimly reads out details of claims surrounding the deaths that occurred on Jurassic Park and the many, many millions of dollars associated with equipment damage, demolition, disposal of facilities, research funds, even media payoffs. He's got the bit between his teeth now and points at the executives, telling them that the madness must stop, that John Hammond has been spending the money in the name of ecology while the stocks have plummeted with no sign of rising again. He mentions the significant product assets that have had to be hidden instead of being harvested and displayed for enormous profit – enough to wipe out the four years of lawsuits and damage control.

"And the one thing, the only thing standing between us and this windfall is Mr. Hammond, a born-again naturalist who happens to be our own CEO. Believe me, I do not enjoy having to say these things about my own uncle. But I don't work for Mother Nature. I work for you." Ludlow pauses as documents are distributed by two assistants to the other board members. He picks his copy up and pointedly begins to ready it aloud, "Whereas the Chief Executive Officer has engaged in wasteful and negligent business practices to further his own personal beliefs;

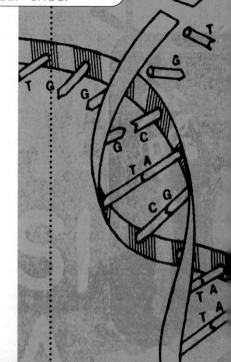

Whereas these practices have affected the financial performance of the company by incurring significant losses; Whereas the shareholders have been materially harmed by these losses; Thereby, be it resolved that John Parker Hammond should be removed from the office of Chief Executive Officer, effective immediately. I move the resolution be put to a vote. Do I have a second?"

The motion is seconded. The hands, some reluctantly and guiltily, slowly begin to rise, unanimously.

New York City

Dr. Ian Malcolm, sits wearily down in the subway train. The events of four years ago have never been out of his mind since. A strange looking man, the type you avoid sitting next to on the subway, approaches him. Malcolm curses under his breath. The man sits down next to him.

"You're him, aren't you?" he grins at Malcolm.

"Excuse me?"

"The guy. The scientist. I saw you on TV," the man leans closer, "I believed you." The man then roars loudly like an animal and Malcolm gets up and moves to a different seat, clearly this is not the first time he's been recognised. Two other commuters begin to stare but look away when Malcolm stares back.

A distressed Malcolm cannot believe his ears.

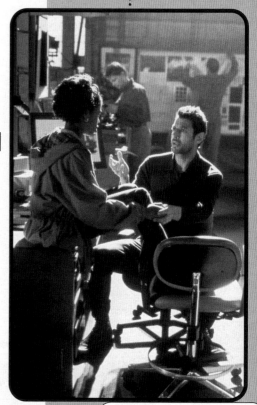

Malcolm tries to reason with Kelly.

The butler eyes the black-clad figure of Dr. Ian Malcolm up and down with a disapproving look. They are clearly not used to such visitors in this expensive Park Avenue apartment.

"Whom shall I tell Mr. Hammond is calling?" he asks the waiting Malcolm.

"I've been summoned," Malcolm replies as the butler turns and walks down the wide hall.

Lex and Tim, both much taller now greet Malcolm with hugs and kisses. He asks them if things are okay. They look past him and remark 'not exactly.' He spots the couple of men in business suits just before Peter Ludlow joins them carrying a sheaf of papers. The two men's eyes meet and there's a flicker of recognition – clearly they don't like each other. Ludlow speaks to his colleagues who present him with some papers requiring his signature.

Ludlow turns to Malcolm, "Well. Dr. Malcolm. Here to share a few campfire stories with my uncle?"

"Do me a favour, Ludlow. Don't ever pretend you and I don't know the truth. You can convince Time magazine and the Sceptical Inquirer of whatever you want, but I was there. I know what happened, and so do you," Malcolm is getting a little upset now.

"You signed a non-disclosure agreement before you went to the island that expressly forbade you from discussing anything you saw. You violated that agreement," Ludlow snaps back.

"And you lied!" Malcolm shouts, "You twisted the facts surrounding the deaths of three people, you stuffed misinformation down the public's throat, which made me look like a nut and hasn't been so good for my livelihood ..."

Ludlow interrupts, "We made a generous compensatory offer for your injuries."

"It was a payoff and an insult. When you spin

Kelly Malcolm.

SITE **B**

CONFIDENTIAL

The expedition enters the waters off Isla Sorna ...

... unaware of their stowaway

The expedition sets up base camp.

> "InGen is my responsibility now, Dr. Malcolm, and I will jealously defend it's interests," Ludlow tells Malcolm, who eyes him suspiciously. "Your responsibility? What about Hammond?"

The stowaway is revealed.

reality, when you cover up evidence, it hurts, it ruins more than just my reputation, it ... ," Malcolm continues before Ludlow cuts in again.

"As I understand it, your university revoked your tenure for selling wild stories to the press, I hardly see how that's my ..."

It's Malcolm's turn now to interrupt, "I didn't sell anything! I didn't take a penny! I told the truth!"

"Your version of it," Ludlow says accusingly.

"There are no versions of the truth. InGen cannot just invent ..."

"InGen is my responsibility now, Dr. Malcolm, and I will jealously defend it's interests," Ludlow tells Malcolm, who eyes him suspiciously.

"Your responsibility? What about Hammond?"

"It is our board of directors which I must look in the eye, not my uncle. Really, you must take my word, these problems of yours are about to be moot. And in a few weeks, they'll be long forgotten."

Malcolm grabs hold of his arm as he walks away and looks him in the face, "Not by me."

Ludlow looks down at Malcolm's firm grip, "This suit cost more than your education."

John Hammond, lies in bed surrounded by medical equipment. He is clearly not a healthy man, yet manages to greet Malcolm cheerily.

"Ian! Don't linger in the doorway like an ingénue, come in!" Malcolm walks towards the bed-stricken Hammond who continues with his greeting, "It's good to see you, it really is. How's the leg?"

"Resentful," Malcolm tells him and then asks, "Why did you want to see me John? Your message said it was important."

"You were right – and I was wrong. There! Did you ever think you'd hear me say such a thing? Spectacularly wrong. Instead of observing those animals, I tried to control them. I squandered an opportunity and we still know next to nothing about their lives. Not their lives as man would have them, behind electric fences, but their behaviour in the wild, the impossible dream of any paleontologist." Hammond pauses for a moment, then, "Thank God for Site B." Malcolm looks blankly at Hammond who smiles back at him, "Well? Didn't it all seem a trifle compact to you? The hatchery, in particular?"

"What are you talking about?" Malcolm asks him, worry evident in his voice.

"You know my initial yields had to be low, far less than one percent, that's a thousand embryos for every single live birth. Genetic engineering on that scale implies a giant operation, not the spotless little laboratory I showed you," Hammond continues as Malcolm grunts and nods, "Isla Nublar was just a showroom, something for the tourists, Site B was the factory floor. It was on Isla Sorna, eighty miles from Nublar. We bred the animals there, nursed them until they were a few months old, then moved them to the park."

"No, no, no, no, no, no …" Malcolm cannot believe what he's hearing.

He stares at Hammond and listens to how, after the events at Jurassic Park a hurricane wiped out the facility on Site B. How the animals were released to mature on their own after the evacuation. How, as Malcolm himself once observed, 'life found a way' and how there is a complete ecological system amongst the dinosaurs – masters of their own world, living in social groups without any interference from outside. For four years John Hammond has fought to keep it from human interference. Malcolm, still in shock, tells him it's the first thing he's done right,

Eddie Carr.

Site B's secret is revealed.

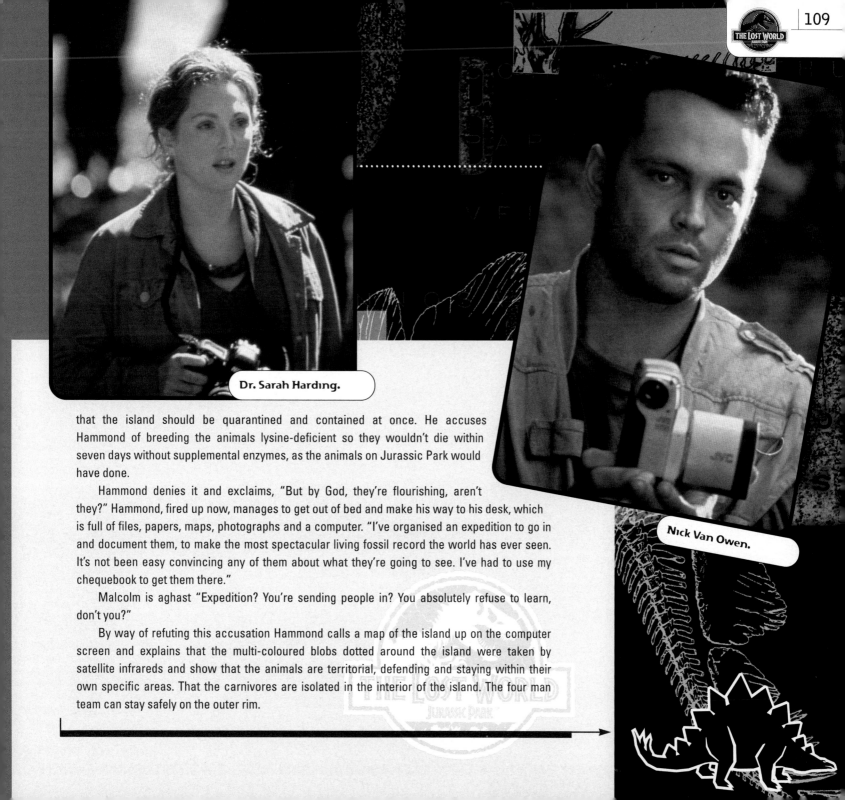

Dr. Sarah Harding.

Nick Van Owen.

that the island should be quarantined and contained at once. He accuses Hammond of breeding the animals lysine-deficient so they wouldn't die within seven days without supplemental enzymes, as the animals on Jurassic Park would have done.

Hammond denies it and exclaims, "But by God, they're flourishing, aren't they?" Hammond, fired up now, manages to get out of bed and make his way to his desk, which is full of files, papers, maps, photographs and a computer. "I've organised an expedition to go in and document them, to make the most spectacular living fossil record the world has ever seen. It's not been easy convincing any of them about what they're going to see. I've had to use my chequebook to get them there."

Malcolm is aghast "Expedition? You're sending people in? You absolutely refuse to learn, don't you?"

By way of refuting this accusation Hammond calls a map of the island up on the computer screen and explains that the multi-coloured blobs dotted around the island were taken by satellite infrareds and show that the animals are territorial, defending and staying within their own specific areas. That the carnivores are isolated in the interior of the island. The four man team can stay safely on the outer rim.

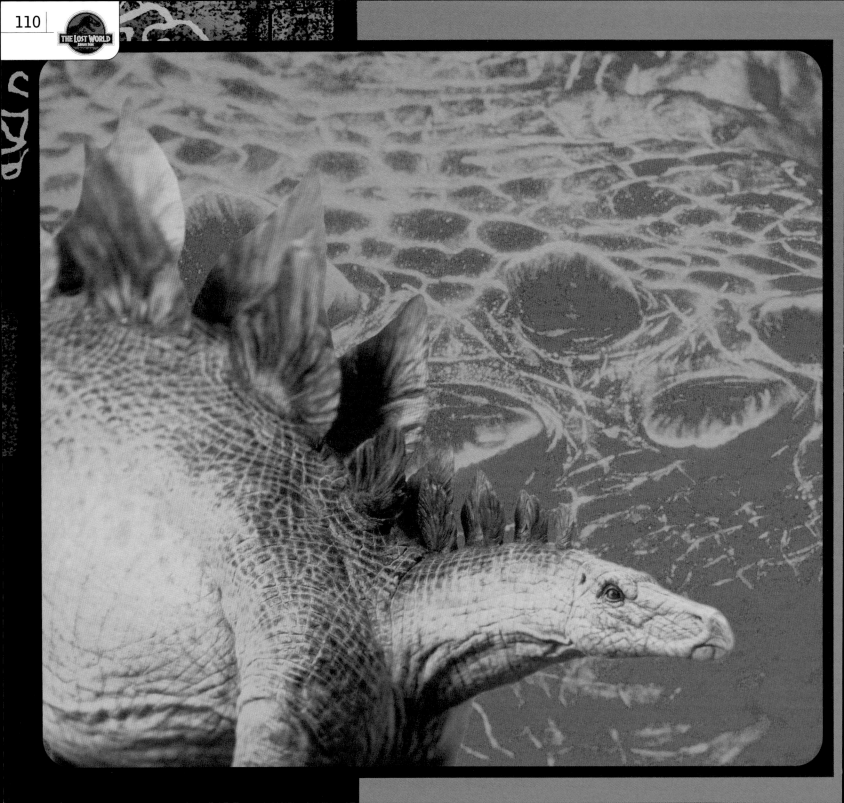

"How did you ever go from capitalist to naturalist in just four years?"

"Four people?! My God, if you must go in there, you go in with the National Guard!" Malcolm explodes. Hammond tells Malcolm that the best results come from animals not knowing they're observed. That one 'observes and documents.' That he's not making the same mistakes again.

"No, you're making all new ones! If you want to observe those animals, you do it safely, by satellite, or helicopter, you don't just barge in there with a camcorder! Who are these four lunatics?" Malcolm is becoming exasperated.

"Nick Van Owen, a video documentarist; Eddie Carr, a field equipment specialist; we also have a paleontologist – and I hope you will be the fourth," Hammond calmly replies.

"John, do you even listen when I speak?"

"Ian, you have always been my harshest critic. If you come out as an advocate with me, we can beat them, I know we can."

"Beat who?"

John Hammond explains to Dr. Ian Malcolm that certain people at InGen have been wanting to exploit Site B for the last four years, to bail the company out of the mess left over from the accident at the park. He tells him about the incident with the British family on the yachting cruise and how control of InGen is being taken away from him. How it is only a matter of time before this 'lost world' is pillaged. But by using documentary evidence and the positive public opinion resulting from it they can keep the animals alive in their natural habitat.

"How did you ever go from capitalist to naturalist in just four years?" Malcolm queries.

"This is my last chance to give something of real value to the world. I can't walk so far to have left no footprints. I will not be known only for my failures, and you are too smart and too proud to let yourself go down in history as a mad scientist. Please. This is a chance at redemption for both of us," Hammond's reply has little effect on Malcolm.

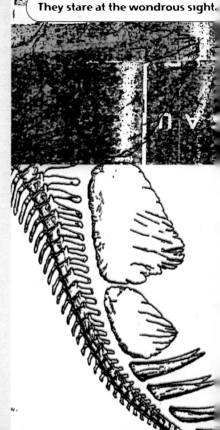

They stare at the wondrous sight.

"That's selfish and grandiose. No, John, of course I won't go. And furthermore, I'm going to contact every member of your team and stop them from going." Malcolm starts looking through a file from the desk, "You didn't mention the name of the paleontologist. Who did you get?"

Hammond looks very uneasy, "She came to me. I just want you to know that. I want to be very clear about who approached whom."

Malcolm looks at him in disbelief, "Who are you talking about?" Hammond blusters as Malcolm cries out, "You didn't bring Sarah into this?!"

"Paleontological behaviour study is a brand new field, and Sarah Harding is on the frontier. Her theories on parenting and nurturing among carnivores have framed the debate for the last five years … ." Hammond tells Malcolm nothing that he already knows.

"Stop right there, just stop," Malcolm rummages through the desk, Hammond asks him what he's doing, "Where's your phone?"

Hammond hesitates, "You're too late – she's already there." Malcolm looks at him, a look of horror spreading across his face, "The others are meeting her in three days."

"You sent my girlfriend to this island alone?" Malcolm is almost in shock. Hammond vainly tries to explain that it was almost impossible to stop Sarah Harding going, even if he wanted to.

"This is criminal, and I will never forgive you for it. You want to leave your name on something, fine, but stop putting it on other people's headstones!" Malcolm reacts badly.

Hammond tries to reassure Malcolm, "She's going to be fine. She's spent years studying African predators, sleeping downwind from lions and so forth – she knows what she's doing. Believe me, the research team will take every possible precautions ..."

"No. It's not a research expedition any more. It's a rescue mission. It's leaving tonight and I'm going with it!"

The Mercedes AAVs (all activity vehicles) are the centre of rapid activity in the large warehouse. Workmen are feverishly modifying the AAVs for the expedition.

Eddie Carr, around forty, is complaining to Dr. Ian Malcolm that it's impossible to have three days taken off his deadline and still have everything ready in time, that nothing's been field tested. Instead of listening to him Malcolm is dialling a bright green satellite phone and getting frustrated.

"Damn it! What's the point of giving her a satellite phone if it doesn't work? What's the matter with it?"

The inquisitive Sarah.

> **"Noble was last year. This year I'm getting paid. Hammond's cheque cleared, that's the only reason I'm going on this wild goose chase."**

Sarah runs for her life

"Could be anything. Solar flares, a satellite out of sync, maybe she even turned it off," Eddie tells him.

"Maybe she doesn't know how to use it," Malcolm wonders.

"You kidding? She faxed me refinements on half the plans for this stuff," Eddie waves his arm around the warehouse as Malcolm bangs the handset, desperately trying to get something out of it.

"Gently. Gently. Ya gotta baby it a little bit. Ya gotta love it."

"I'll love it when it works," Malcolm retorts.

"And it'll work when you love it," Eddie makes his point.

Nick Van Owen's white van, the worse for wear, screeches to a halt in the middle of the garage floor. A good looking man, late twenties gets out and thanks Eddie for the two minute warning. Eddie makes the introductions as Nick unloads his substantial photographic equipment.

"Nick Van Owen, Ian Malcolm. Nick's our field photographer."

"What's your background? Wildlife photography?" Malcolm asks, determined not to be impressed.

"Wildlife, combat, you name it. When I was with Nightline I was in Rwanda, Chechnya, all over Bosnia. Do some volunteer for Greenpeace once in a while."

Malcolm rolls his eyes, "Greenpeace, yeah, that's just what we need. What drew you there?"

"Women. 'Bout eighty percent female in Greenpeace," Nick tells Malcolm, knowing this won't impress him.

"Very noble," Malcolm dryly comments.

"Noble was last year. This year I'm getting paid. Hammond's cheque cleared, that's the only reason I'm going on this wild goose chase."

The stegosaurus swings its spike

Sarah heads for cover and escapes death by inches.

The party flee.

"Where you're going is the only place in the world where the geese chase you."

Malcolm tries to reason with Sarah.

"Where you're going is the only place in the world where the geese chase you," Malcolm points out to Nick Van Owen, who merely shrugs.

A workman shouts down his apologies to Eddie as a large metal crate falls from the top of the make-shift scaffolding, "Sorry, Eddie. Specs say it can't deform at 12,000 PSI, we had to test it!"

Eddie explains to Malcolm, the sound of the crashing crate still ringing in his ears, that the cage goes on top of a titanium scaffold – so the researchers can safely observe. Malcolm cynically notes that they may just be at the right height for being bitten.

A twelve year old African-American girl stands behind the group, watching the proceedings with interest. Malcolm turns around and greets his daughter, Kelly. Malcolm and Kelly use Eddie's office – Kelly has already sussed that Malcolm hadn't asked to meet her to chat about the weather, she knows he's going away – again. She looks down at the slip of paper with the address of an old family friend on and is clearly not happy about staying there. Malcolm tries to reason with her, Kelly points out some of Malcolm's deficiencies in the fatherhood department.

He tells her she can always concentrate on the gymnastics team while he's away and then looks sheepish when Kelly tells him she was cut from the team months ago and he didn't even remember. Throughout the conversation the tannoy keeps calling Malcolm's name, he has to go and see what Eddie wants. Malcolm feebly says goodbye to his daughter.

Kelly watches her father and Eddie in deep discussion as she leaves the office. She looks around the massive trailers in the garage, two of them joined together ready to be towed away. Nobody notices Kelly sneak inside the front trailer.

An awful lot of thought and design have gone into the layout and content of the trailer. There's a biological laboratory area with all the necessary equipment, computers and processors and a communications section. A large map on the wall has the Pacific island of 'Sorna' circled.

The waters off Isla Sorna.

The barge, carrying the two trailers and two AAVs makes it's way through the choppy waters to the island. Malcolm tries to contact Sarah on the phone – again, no luck. Eddie opens a metal case and tells Malcolm about the Lindstradt air rifle that fires a subsonic Fluger impact-delivery dart, a dart that carries a venom so lethal that it acts within two-thousandths of a second. Malcolm grunts, hoping it works better than Eddie's satellite phone.

Suddenly, through the mist, they can see the high cliffs of Isla Sorna and the boat makes for a narrow inlet. It heads deeper inland and eventually beaches at a tropical lagoon and the unloading begins. Nick translates to Eddie and Malcolm as the Captain of the boat nervously looks around. He's not going to drop anchor off the island, there are too many stories about fishermen who visited here and were never seen again. They can call him on the radio or the satellite phone – he can be back in two hours. But he won't stay near this group of islands – the islands they call 'The Five Deaths.'

Isla Sorna.

Eddie explains about the cone shaped receiving dish on top of one of the trailers. The Global Positioning Sensor uses radar and navigational satellites and coming up on the hand-held

Malcolm's intent on leaving the madness.

The InGen hunting party arrives.

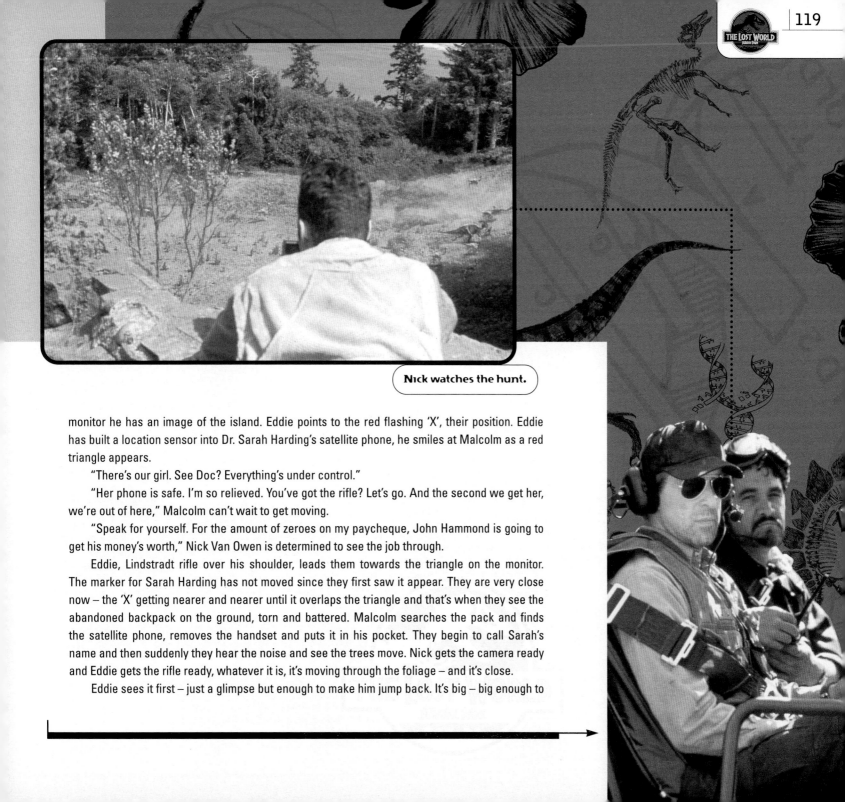

Nick watches the hunt.

monitor he has an image of the island. Eddie points to the red flashing 'X', their position. Eddie has built a location sensor into Dr. Sarah Harding's satellite phone, he smiles at Malcolm as a red triangle appears.

"There's our girl. See Doc? Everything's under control."

"Her phone is safe. I'm so relieved. You've got the rifle? Let's go. And the second we get her, we're out of here," Malcolm can't wait to get moving.

"Speak for yourself. For the amount of zeroes on my paycheque, John Hammond is going to get his money's worth," Nick Van Owen is determined to see the job through.

Eddie, Lindstradt rifle over his shoulder, leads them towards the triangle on the monitor. The marker for Sarah Harding has not moved since they first saw it appear. They are very close now – the 'X' getting nearer and nearer until it overlaps the triangle and that's when they see the abandoned backpack on the ground, torn and battered. Malcolm searches the pack and finds the satellite phone, removes the handset and puts it in his pocket. They begin to call Sarah's name and then suddenly they hear the noise and see the trees move. Nick gets the camera ready and Eddie gets the rifle ready, whatever it is, it's moving through the foliage – and it's close.

Eddie sees it first – just a glimpse but enough to make him jump back. It's big – big enough to

The hunt gathers pace.

> **"This is — this is magnificent!" Eddie can't get over the sight of the dinosaurs.**
>
> **"Yeah, 'oooh,' 'aaah,' that's how it always starts. Screaming and running comes later."**

worry about. The fins on the back of the stegosaur come into view first and the rest follows through in a gap in the foliage. A small head, thick neck, huge body and a dragging, spiked tail. Another one, much smaller, follows as they watch open-mouthed. The third, and largest, comes out of the foliage and walks within feet of the group, paying no attention to them whatsoever, others come into view. They follow the dinosaurs into the bush. In the clearing they see the small herd, eight in total, infants and adults. They stare at the wondrous sight, Nick shooting rapidly with his SLR camera.

He moves down into the stream and takes more photographs. He is so absorbed that he doesn't notice Sarah Harding only a few feet from him, taking some pictures with her small automatic. They notice each, laugh and go through a warm greeting. Malcolm and Eddie come on the scene.

"This is — this is magnificent!" Eddie can't get over the sight of the dinosaurs.

"Yeah, 'oooh,' 'aaah,' that's how it always starts. Screaming and running comes later," Malcolm sceptically notes as Sarah makes her way over to them. She whispers excitedly, greeting her boyfriend briefly and then talking breathlessly about the dinosaurs and her observations since being on the island. Malcolm listens patiently but not with interest, holds up the battered back-pack and asks her if she was attacked. Sarah replies that it's her lucky backpack and it always looks like that. She borrows Nick's superior camera, and checking the shutter's in silent mode, she rushes off to photograph the herd. The others watch, impressed as she gets closer and closer, fearless. From behind a small group of rocks she can see the nest and the baby stego. She gets close enough and gently strokes the animal's snout, smiling broadly as she does so.

As she shoots the last picture the rewind mechanism kicks in and the camera suddenly sounds very loud. The alpha male, the largest, turns round far quicker than one would have thought, the back plates bristling with alertness. It moves towards Sarah. Malcolm worriedly calls out her name and the stego swings round, the tail lashing through the air towards Sarah. She jumps back just as the tail crashes into the ground, quickly she moves away and scrambles into a hollow log as the tail comes down again. The log breaks in half as the spiked tail cuts

A pachycephalosaur tries to evade capture.

through it, right in front of Sarah's face. She crawls out as the stego lets out a loud roar, frees it's tail and disappears into the bush with the rest of the herd.

Far from shaken, Sarah hugs Malcolm "Isn't it great!" Malcolm just pulls her phone out from his pocket and tells her that when it rings, answer it!

Along the trail back to the base camp, Nick carefully unloads the prized film and dreams loudly of the Pulitzer Prize. Eddie is still stunned and almost speechless as Sarah and Malcolm argue. She didn't tell Malcolm she was coming here because he would have tried to stop her. Sarah tries to change the subject by telling Malcolm that she's figured out how the animals survive without lysine – by eating agama beans, soya or similar lysine-rich vegetation the herbivores can survive. And the carnivores eat the herbivores.

She breaks off when she sees Nick preparing to smoke a cigarette – dinosaurs can pick up scents from miles away she tells him. The argument now turns to the point of studying the dinosaurs. Malcolm obviously wants to get the hell out of here and Sarah wants to stay – making the point that all predators are obsessively territorial and that those territories are all situated in the centre of the island. Stay away from there, and from the game trails they hunt on, and it's perfectly safe – Malcolm disagrees, they go where there's food and this expedition is going home.

"What is this. You don't usually care about what continent I'm on, now you charge in here on a white horse. What do you think you're doing?" Sarah angrily asks him.

"Hey, someone who loves you travels five thousand miles to tell you your life is in danger and you want to start a fight?"

"You love me?" Sarah is taken aback.

"Baby, I've never been so mental over a chick, you know that," he tells her.

"Why didn't you ever say so, butthead?" Sarah looks deep into his eyes.

"I did. In the hospital. In Costa Rica," Malcolm replies.

"You were on painkillers. You said it to the anaesthesiologist."

"Sarah, please. You've seen the place, you've drawn some pretty impressive conclusions, people are going to sit up and take notice, believe me, now let's go," Malcolm pleads. Sarah begins to explain how her research can change the way dinosaurs are perceived when Nick rushes by – towards the plume of smoke rising above the trees. They follow him and the direction of the smoke, to the base camp.

The hunters close in on their quarry

> "I'm taking my daughter out of here. Anybody who's coming with me, this is your last chance to get out," Malcolm calls out and is totally ignored.

They kick dirt over the campfire, Sarah pointing out that water makes smoke billow.

"Who the hell started a campfire?!" Malcolm demands, furiously.

"It was just to make dinner," a sheepish Kelly Malcolm tells her father from the doorway of the trailer, "I wanted it ready when you got back."

Malcolm is trying to make a call on the satellite phone as he argues with his daughter. Neither attempt is very successful. Sarah points out to Malcolm that Kelly got her curiosity from him as Malcolm tells Kelly she has no idea what's going on here. Kelly scores some good girl points by answering that she does know what's going on and, although nobody else believed him, she always did. Malcolm is touched, but soon angry again when the phone still won't work.

Sarah tells Eddie that if they want to use the high hide, the large observation cage, there's a good spot in the middle of some palms a hundred yards away. They have a heavy scent and are toxic to the animals. When Eddie tells her the cage is fifteen feet from the ground, Sarah declines to join them – a fear of heights. Malcolm, listening to the conversation, sarcastically suggests they smear themselves with sheep's blood. He asks Eddie if there's any chance the radio in the trailer might work – Eddie, getting a little tired of all this, suggests he tries flicking the switch to the 'on' position.

"I'm taking my daughter out of here. Anybody who's coming with me, this is your last chance to get out," Malcolm calls out and is totally ignored, the others continue to make plans. He leaves the phone and moves towards the trailer as Sarah warns the others about leaving any kind of scent, no hair tonics, no cologne, no insect repellent, all food to be sealed in plastic bags. No one has noticed the low hum in the distance.

The ruthless Roland Tembo.

Kelly watches the horrific hunt.

Tembo barks orders at Dieter.

The sound suddenly bursts through the air and it's deafening, roaring overhead. The huge military helicopters, flying low, pass by as they look up in disbelief. Large cargo containers and vehicles sway below the undercarriages.

Everyone rushes and stops at the edge of a ridge as the helicopters hover and begin to descend. Eddie can clearly see the 'InGen' logo on the choppers. He wonders aloud why would Hammond send two teams? Malcolm grabs the binoculars and looks at the activity all around the helicopters.

"Hammond didn't send these guys. It's Peter Ludlow," he almost spits the words out.

"What do they want?" Sarah questions.

"They want their money back," Nick Van Owen perceptively comments.

They move along the ridge, below them a mixed herd of herbivores, hadrosaurs, pachycephalosaurs and gallimimuses, all medium sized dinosaurs, are racing hard across the plain. Malcolm swings the binoculars round and then he sees the pursuing vehicles. Two herding jeeps, one motorcycle, a fast mini-jeep, a container truck and a pick-up truck.

The noise of the hunt thunders across the plain. Peter Ludlow shouts instructions into the walkie-talkie, how he wants base camp setting up on the plain – as soon as they've finished. A voice tells him to cancel the order, the authoritative voice of Roland Tembo, seasoned game hunter, English and hard as nails. He cancels Ludlow's order and then explains why.

"This is a game trail, Mr. Ludlow. Carnivores hunt on game trails. Do you want to set up base camp or a buffet." Ludlow cancels the order. Tembo continues "Peter, if you want me to run your little camping trip, there are two conditions. First – I'm in charge and when I'm not around Dieter is. Your job is to sign the cheques, tell us we're doing a good job, and open your case of Scotch when we have a good day. Second condition – my fee. You can keep it. All I want is the right to hunt one of the tyrannosaurs. A male. Buck only. Why and how are my business. If you don't like either of those conditions, you're on your own. Go ahead and set up your camp right here, or in the middle of a rex nest for all I care. But I've been on too many safaris with rich dentists to listen to any more suicidal ideas. Okay?"

"Okay," Ludlow concedes, quickly learning that Roland Tembo is not a man to argue with.

"Good lad," Roland nods and pulls himself up into the vehicles specially made reconnaissance tower. He has a perfect view of the hunt. He signals to the pursuit vehicle at the side to accelerate past them. The 'snagger' has a long metal pole with a noose at the end high in the air. Sat near the other end of the pole is Dieter Stark, South African, mid-forties and extremely mean, tranquilliser rifle at the ready.

The herd is heading for the jungle, away from the now dangerous plain. A motorcycle swings in from the side, cutting the herd off. Tembo shouts orders into the walkie-talkie as the vehicles hunt down the dinosaurs.

From the jungle two huge, startled apatosaurs, their long necks craning into the sky, run out onto the plain. The herd follows them along, some running between their legs. The motorcycle follows under the apatosaur in hot pursuit of a small pachycephalosaur. The animal is isolated as the two pursuit vehicles help to cut it off. The pachy has stopped. Dr. Robert Burke, complete with cowboy hat, shoulder length hair and John Lennon glasses stares at the animal, wide-eyed. Two hunters now approach the pachy, lassos at the ready, walking slowly. Another vehicle pulls up and a hunter begins to get out, that's when the pachy charges. It's skull, nine inches solid and domed, crashes into the open door sending the hunter hurtling back inside and out of the other

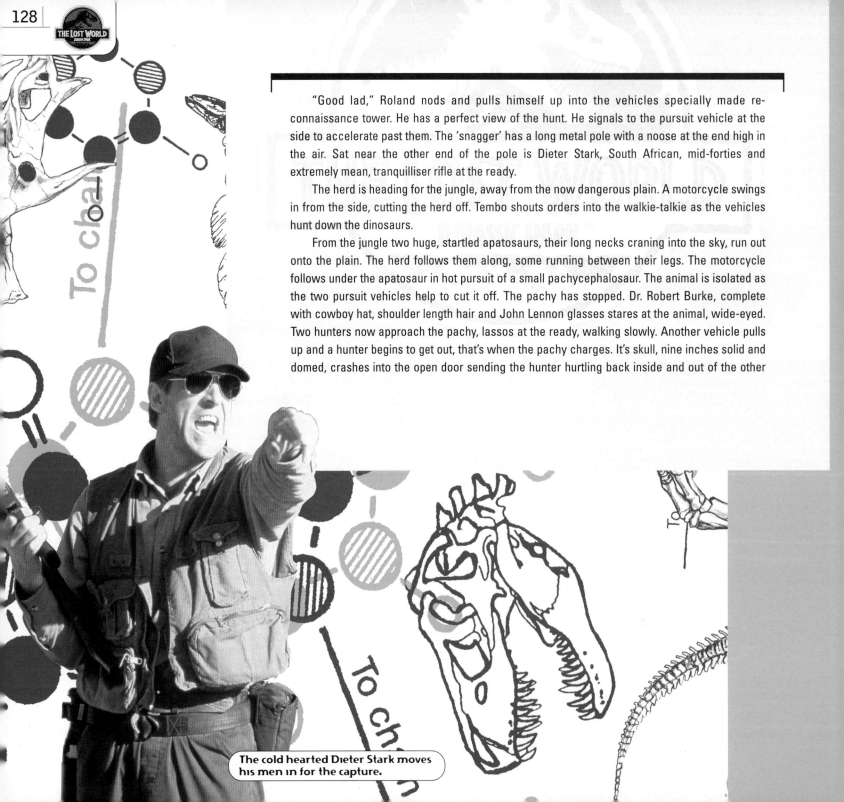

The cold hearted Dieter Stark moves his men in for the capture.

Peter Ludlow looks on.

door. The tranquilliser dart strikes the animal in the neck, the noose follows shortly afterwards. It's quickly caged and loaded onto the back of the containment truck. The hunters quickly join the hunt again.

Roland Tembo barks orders at Dieter, telling him he's close to a carinthosaur. Dieter shouts back 'what?' and Roland, frustrated with the long and difficult names, shouts "The one with the big red horn, the pompadour! Elvis!" A tranquilliser dart stops the animal as Dieter shoots from a telescopic seat that extends four feet out. The carinthosaur doesn't go down – it stands groggy and confused as the hunters warily surround it, then they have it. The hunters have come fully prepared – there is no escape for the animal.

Dieter, thirsty from the hunt, drinks from a canteen. The small compsognathus, just like the one that frightened the little girl from the yacht, hops over to a puddle near Dieter's foot. Dr. Burke is delighted by it's presence. Dieter asks if it's dangerous and Burke replies no, they're scavengers feeding on the dead or wounded. The compy's interested in Dieters boot now.

Dr. Burke.

The party are stunned.

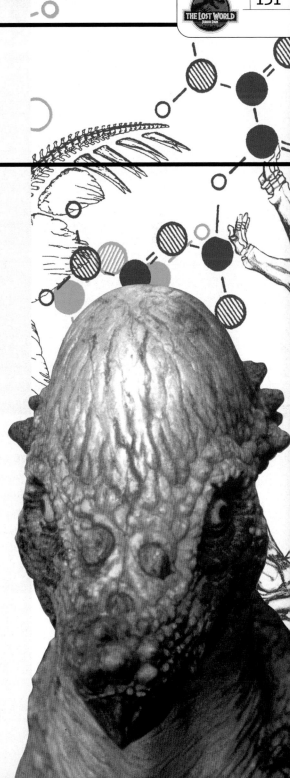

"If the nest is upwind, so are we. When he comes back, he'll know we're here before we have a chance. The trick is to get him to come where we are," Roland decides.

"It gives me the creeps. It's like it's not scared," Dieter looks down at the compy.

"Probably because there haven't been any visitors to the island. It has no reason to fear man," Burke, still fascinated, replies. Dieter pulls a steel rod from his belt and presses a button. He puts it on the compy's back and an electric shock shoots through the animal's small body, throwing it head over heels. It dashes into the bushes, hurt and crying.

"Now it does," Dieter walks away.

Roland calls Dr. Burke over and asks him if he recognises the large, deep footprint. Grimly Burke tells him he does – tyrannosaurus rex. Ajay, Roland's trusted tracker on many campaigns, points to the trail leading to the jungle and the other set of tracks, those of a smaller animal, carried away by the rex. Roland goes to his jeep and opens a wood and leather case and removes the magnificent antique elephant gun. A double-barrelled .600 Nitro Express. The barrels extend two feet, an ivory bead foresight sits at the end. He loads the four inch long, three quarters of an inch wide cartridges into the gun and he and Ajay head into the jungle. Ludlow calls out, asking Roland where he's going.

"To collect my fee," he shouts back over his shoulder and he's gone.

With some difficulty and a great deal of skill they find the tyrannosaur nest, ten feet in diameter and surrounded by walls of earth. In the nest the baby tyrannosaur, four and a half feet long, squeaks continuously and feeds on the remains of a dead animal. Other carcasses and bones litter the nest. Ajay asks Roland if they should wait for the return of the buck.

"If the nest is upwind, so are we. When he comes back, he'll know we're here before we have a chance. The trick is to get him to come where we are," Roland decides.

In the hunter's base camp tents are being erected around a central campfire. All the vehicles are parked together at one end of the camp. At the opposite end are the cages containing the day's spoils. A camera, connected to a satellite dish, is being set up and the lights, glowing brightly in the growing dark, are already for the transmission from the inside of the open tent.

The hunters' intentions are debated

Malcolm, Sarah, Nick, Eddie and Kelly, all still in shock from the horrific hunt they have witnessed, look down at the scene below them. Sarah notes that they've only captured small herbivores before she gets dizzy from the height and retreats to safer ground. Malcolm concludes that the reason Hammond wanted them all to get here quickly was to get the research done before Ludlow and his men arrived – Hammond knew they were coming. Kelly wonders why they want to build another park, after what happened the last time.

"They're not building anything, they're taking those animals out of here. Back to the mainland. I can't believe what I'm seeing. And I can't believe it's all run by Ludlow," Malcolm tells everyone.

"It isn't. Check out the guy walking past the fire," Nick points Roland Tembo out. "I've run into this customer before, in Brazil. He was spearhunting jaguars. He's the one in charge. Look, you should all know, Hammond told me these guys might show up. He honestly thought we'd have time to finish before they got here. But in case we didn't, he sent a back-up plan." Sarah asks what back-up plan.

"Me," and with that Nick pulls from his pack a bolt cutter, a hunting knife and a pry bar.

"Sarah. I must get Kelly off this island now. So, I'll ask one more time, and not again, are you coming with us?" Malcolm stares at Sarah. She looks back and then at Nick as he puts the tools into his belt with a definite purpose about them.

"I've waited a lifetime for this opportunity. I won't let them take it away," Sarah says, and it's definite.

"You wouldn't either, Dad. You'd be trying to stop those guys yourself if I wasn't here," Kelly looks up at her father.

"Not under deteriorating circumstances like these, it's a bad time and the wrong place."

"You wouldn't care, it's how you are," Kelly turns to Sarah "once somebody makes him mad, he can't help himself".

Malcolm, losing the battle, rambles on about statistical phenomenon. How when things are going bad they stay bad. Bad things cluster, they go to hell together.

"They're about to. For them," Nick waits at the end of the ridge. Sarah, looking down and frightened, joins him.

"Where'd you get this fear of heights?" Nick asks.

"Dating tall men," Sarah looks straight at Malcolm before her and Nick, hand in hand, scramble down the hillside.

The first sign of Tembo's prize.

> "Rex won't be any different. It'll come."
>
> "You're kidding yourself, or I'd be worried.
> An adult T-rex doesn't care about it's young,
> it cares about one thing — filling it's own belly."

The baby tyrannosaur squeals loudly and tries to free itself from the chain attached to the stake in the ground. Ludlow approaches Roland in the small jungle clearing and asks him about the gun.

"My father's .600 Nitro Express. Made in 1904. Karimojo Bell gave it to him after he took down his last elephant. 8700 foot pounds of striking force, each barrel."

"How close do you have to be?" Ludlow asks.

"Forty yards. Less, maybe. I assume it'll take a slug in the brain case to bring him down," Roland replies.

"Why not just use a scope and a poison dart and snipe him from a hill?"

"Or a laser beam from a satellite?" Roland remarks, disgusted.

"You think this'll draw the adult?"

"I once saw a bull elephant kill itself charging a jeep. All the jeep had done was startle the bull's calves. I saw a lioness carry wounded prey four and a half miles, all the way back to it's den, just to teach it's cubs how to finish off a kill."

"Killing lessons? Heart-warming," Ludlow remarks, rather sarcastically.

"Rex won't be any different. It'll come."

"You're kidding yourself, or I'd be worried. An adult T-rex doesn't care about it's young, it cares about one thing — filling it's own belly. It acts the way people wish they could, that's why everyone's fascinated by it. If people had the chance to see one dinosaur and one only, ninety-nine percent would choose the tyrannosaur. Now that's something to build a theme park round," Ludlow seems impressed by his own knowledge.

"You could never contain it."

"Sure, there's sedatives for that, growth inhibitors, surgery to shorten its tendons, make it immobile," Ludlow bends closer to the baby rex "but you wouldn't be any trouble at all, would you? And the entire world would pay to watch you grow up. You're a billion dollar idea, my little …"

A small animal rushes through the clearing just behind Ludlow. Frightened, he whirls round

The hunters' base camp is being watched.

Sabotage — the only solution.

Ludlow prepares to show off his capture.

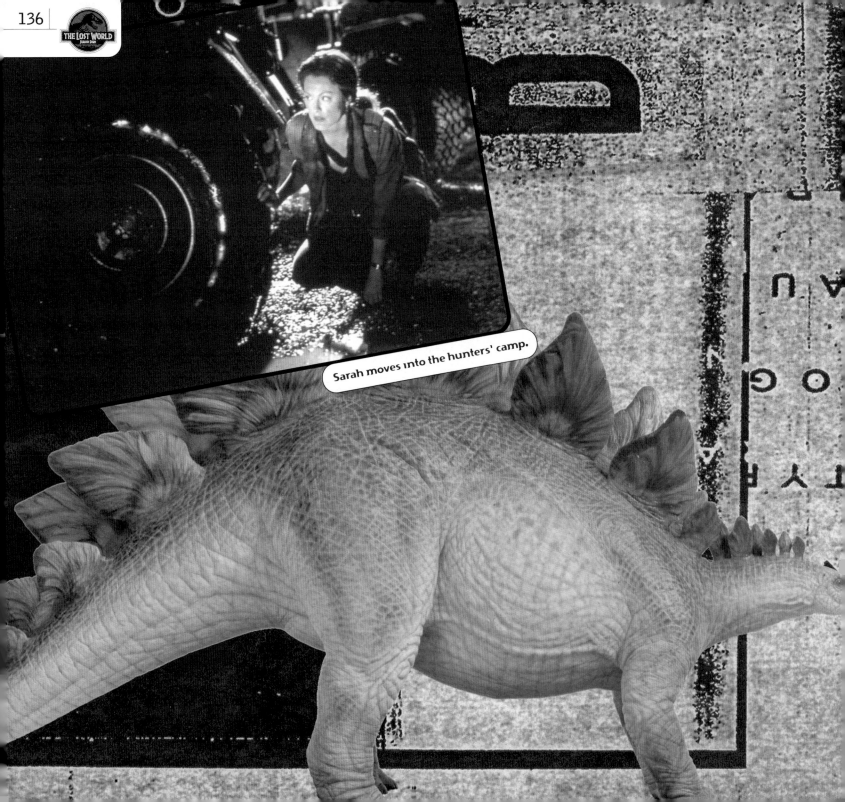

Sarah moves into the hunters' camp.

and falls on top of the rex. A sickening crunch and the baby screams in pain as it's leg snaps.

"Damn it, you've broken its leg!" Roland shouts at the none too pleased Ludlow. Ludlow, who is more upset at the possible loss of financial potential than the animal's condition, begins to walk back to the camp.

Roland calls after him, "Orwell had a point, didn't he? – Four legs good, two legs bad."

"What?" Ludlow asks.

"It's what the animals said, Mr. Ludlow. Just before they took over the farm."

As Ludlow enters the camp a voice calls out to him that they're ready to transmit, board directors and potential investors are assembled at the InGen boardroom in San Diego. He hurries over to the open tent and the satellite equipment.

At the edge of the camp Nick and Sarah are watching and waiting. As the transmission begins and everyone's attention is drawn to it, they move into the camp. The screeching of the baby T-rex begins to ring out in the night.

Roland and Ajay watch the area around the baby from their vantage point in a nearby tree. Broken branches weaved together to form their very own high hide.

Nick and Sarah now begin to loosen the bolts on the cages. The animals, getting excited, begin to make more and more noise.

Ludlow has the satellite phone to his ear and addresses the camera. The tent has a map on display showing the island and where the different species of dinosaurs can be found. Two captured and caged compys are on display.

Ludlow can see the board directors of InGen and half a dozen potential investors on the computer screen, they can see him in San Diego.

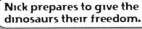

Nick prepares to give the dinosaurs their freedom.

"Simply put, InGen is seeking limited partners to defray some of our expansion costs. The prospectus you've been given by the board explicitly details our projected hardware and construction expenses, and, as you can see by my two friends here with me tonight, the 'software' is already fully developed," Ludlow points to the compy's and the folk in San Diego get closer to the screen to look at a tiny part of their future investment.

Outside the biggest cage, Nick pulls out the bolt cutters. Sarah looks at the triceratops, the largest of the captured beasts, about ten feet high and almost as wide.

"Hang on. We may get some turbulence," Nick smiles at Sarah.

Ludlow continues, really getting going now "... but you don't send people halfway around the world to a zoo, you bring the zoo to them. And San Diego is the perfect setting. People already associate our city with animal attractions – Sea World, the San Diego Zoo. Mr Hammond knew that, before he ever dreamed of an island, he started construction on an amphitheatre right near where you're sitting – in the InGen waterfront complex. But he abandoned it in favour of something far grander and, ultimately, impossible. And that facility sits unused, unfinished, when it could be completed and ready to receive visitors in less than a month. Gentlemen, these animals are product

Tembo finds the bait for his prized T-rex — its baby.

Startled by the commotion.

assets that will generate revenue immediately, they are fully grown and fully … fully …"

The tent begins to vibrate, there's a rumble – getting louder. People are beginning to shout and scream and the triceratop thunders through the back of the tent.

Men and equipment are bowled over as the animal charges on, the canvas wrapped around it's huge body, causing pandemonium everywhere. Men run in all directions away from the path of destruction as the animal, blinded by the canvas stomps into the campfire. The canvas, now alight, causes the animal to panic even further, it crashes into the other tents and now spreads fire in it's wake.

The triceratop smashes into the side of a jeep, it rolls towards the largest of the tents, it's fuel spilling and suddenly flames shoot up and the jeep explodes.

In the tree, all thoughts of the T-rex are forgotten as the noise of the chaos in the camp shatters the calm of the evening. As they look over the trees, more flames shoot up in the air as more vehicles begin to blaze and explode. The burning jeep flies over the treetops and they leap from the tree as the jeep crashes into it.

The other animals are now free and running riot as Nick and Sarah flee into the

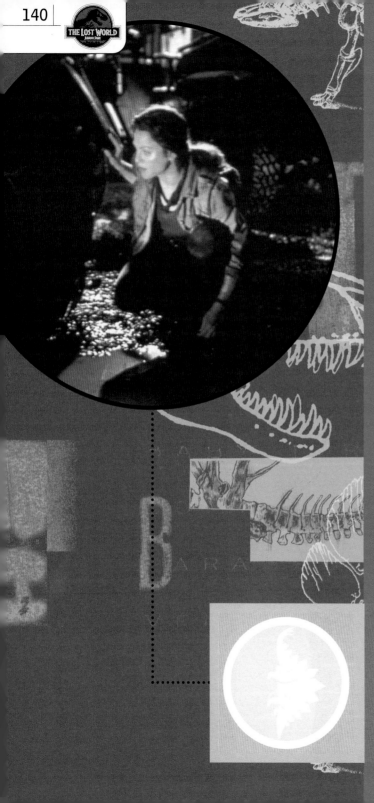

STEGO

One of the many caged beasts
unaware of Sarah.

"Last time I leave you in charge," Roland tells the bruised and battered Dieter.

jungle. The equipment tent, now on fire, explodes sending Dieter to the ground. Wearily he pulls himself up and looks to see the approaching Roland Tembo.

"Last time I leave you in charge," Roland tells the bruised and battered Dieter.

As Sarah and Nick run from the camp they come across the clearing – and the baby T-rex, still chained to the stake. They pull the stake out of the ground, taking care not to damage the animal's broken leg and carry it to the waiting AAV.

Roland and Ludlow survey the camp, or what's left of it. Roland holds up one of the broken padlocks and concludes that they are not alone on the island.

In the back of the car the baby tyrannosaur is screaming in pain and anger as the car crashes through the jungle. Sarah screams at Nick to close the window – or every predator in the jungle is going to hear it.

The triceratops awaits it's fate.

Close to the trailers, back at base camp, Eddie is about to raise the high hide. The small cage already in position on top of the struts, the electric winch already attached to the front of the AAV. Before he can raise it into the tree the other AAV pulls up. He watches, wide-eyed, as Sarah and Nick remove the wounded T-rex from the back of the car.

In the trailer, Malcolm and Kelly are trying to get the radio to work. Malcolm's efforts have so far resulted in a nonsensical conversation with someone who has probably never spoken a word of English in her life. Kelly finds a log book and they look up relevant frequencies. Malcolm turns the dial, cutting through static, he's about to make contact. Just as Sarah, Nick and the screaming T-rex burst into the trailer, the animal struggling furiously.

"Hi, Ian. No lectures, please," Sarah needn't have bothered speaking – Malcolm can't, his jaw is almost to the ground.

As Nick holds the infant down, Sarah gets the medical supplies and plunges the syringe into the animal's thigh. Malcolm and Kelly look on. Kelly loving every minute of it and Malcolm just managing to string together the words "I am aghast." Sarah, her shirt covered in the T-rex's blood, now runs a small ultrasound transducer over it's leg. They identify the exact nature of the

A disappointed Tembo with Dieter.

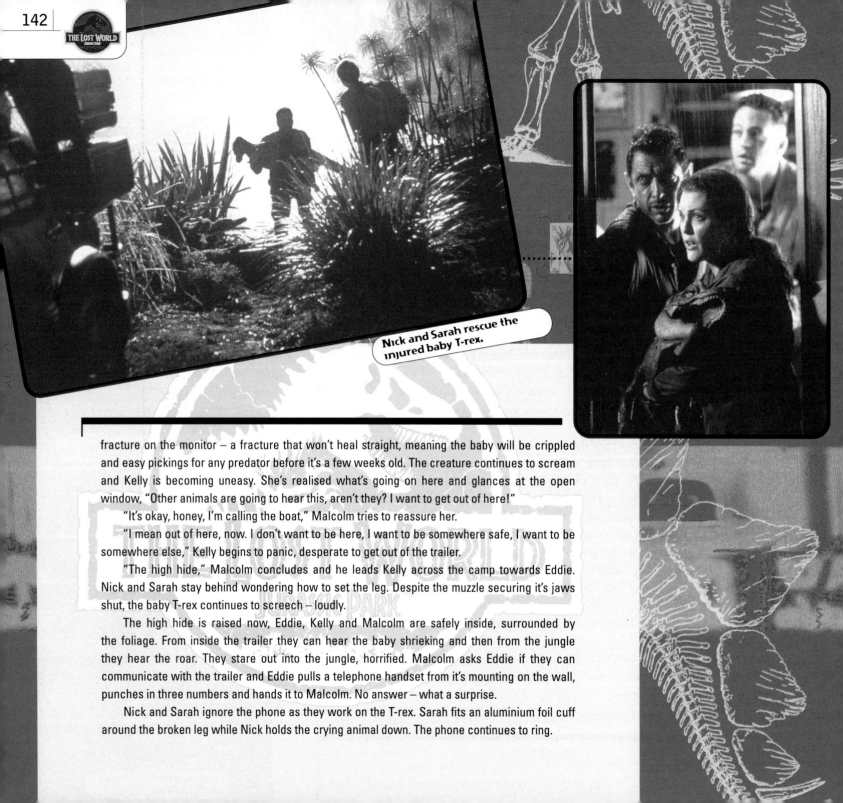

Nick and Sarah rescue the injured baby T-rex.

fracture on the monitor – a fracture that won't heal straight, meaning the baby will be crippled and easy pickings for any predator before it's a few weeks old. The creature continues to scream and Kelly is becoming uneasy. She's realised what's going on here and glances at the open window, "Other animals are going to hear this, aren't they? I want to get out of here!"

"It's okay, honey, I'm calling the boat," Malcolm tries to reassure her.

"I mean out of here, now. I don't want to be here, I want to be somewhere safe, I want to be somewhere else," Kelly begins to panic, desperate to get out of the trailer.

"The high hide," Malcolm concludes and he leads Kelly across the camp towards Eddie. Nick and Sarah stay behind wondering how to set the leg. Despite the muzzle securing it's jaws shut, the baby T-rex continues to screech – loudly.

The high hide is raised now, Eddie, Kelly and Malcolm are safely inside, surrounded by the foliage. From inside the trailer they can hear the baby shrieking and then from the jungle they hear the roar. They stare out into the jungle, horrified. Malcolm asks Eddie if they can communicate with the trailer and Eddie pulls a telephone handset from it's mounting on the wall, punches in three numbers and hands it to Malcolm. No answer – what a surprise.

Nick and Sarah ignore the phone as they work on the T-rex. Sarah fits an aluminium foil cuff around the broken leg while Nick holds the crying animal down. The phone continues to ring.

Malcolm realises he must go down and warn them. Eddie fits one of the rope descenders around Malcolm and he begins the drop as Kelly pleads with him to stay. The roar from the jungle sounds again – louder and nearer. A flock of birds shoot up into the sky and the tree tops begin to rapidly sway as Malcolm tears across to the trailer. Eddie raises the Lindstradt looking for the predator. The cage and the trees move – the animal has passed beneath them.

The baby is thrashing about now as Sarah makes another injection to calm it down. Malcolm bursts through the door and grabs the ringing phone and screams at Sarah, "Just once in your life would it kill you to pick it up?! Help me get this thing out of here!" He begins to lift the baby rex into his arms as a roar and a crash loudly sound outside the trailer. They quickly turn to the window to see the AAV rolling over.

"What is it?" Sarah asks, frightened now.

"Mommy's very angry," Malcolm replies.

Again the roar, and the baby answers back. The huge head of the full grown tyrannosaurus rex looks through the window of the trailer. Inside all three simply freeze, terrified. The infant is calmer now, responding to the calls from the parent. Another roar, louder and from the other side of the trailer.

"Make that mommy and daddy," Malcolm, voice trembling, observes.

Kelly cannot believe her eyes.

The look of terror on his face,
"Hang on. This is going to be bad."

"This isn't hunting behaviour! Not hunting – they're searching, Ian! They came for their baby!" Sarah cries out.

"Let's not disappoint them," Malcolm tells Sarah and they carry the baby to the opposite end of the trailer. The two rexes outside follow their path along the length of the trailer. They reach the door – Sarah, shaking badly, begins to sing 'Born Free' as the baby wriggles free and onto the ground outside. Malcolm closes the door and they listen to the attentive sounds of the parents inspecting their child. The sound of huge, departing footsteps follows and the phone rings. It's Eddie telling them the family is going back to the jungle.

All three, drained from nervous exhaustion, slump against the wall. Sarah, relieved, excitedly speaks of the parental instincts of tyrannosaurus – how the book must be re-written, how the debate is now over. Nick has got to say something to the others.

"There's an unwritten rule when a news crew is in a war zone. You stop the van every two miles and decide whether or not you feel lucky. One 'no' from anybody in the group and you turn around right there, no questions asked, nobody embarrassed. So – do we go on?"

"No!" all three shout at once and laugh out loud. Malcolm gets up and picks up the microphone to call the boat. The phone rings again, the laughter stops as they all anxiously stare at it. Malcolm, immediately thinking of Kelly, opens the door, steps outside and straight back in again. The look of terror on his face, "Hang on. This is going to be bad."

The T-rex smashes into the side of the trailer almost knocking it over. A crack of electricity and the trailer plunges into darkness. Nick looks out of the window and sees the T-rex move by and then he sees the other one, head down, thundering towards the trailer! All hang on to the nearest solid object they can find. The impact sends the trailer, the rear of the two trailers, over and over – it rests upside down. They fall from the floor to the ceiling, along with everything else that isn't bolted down. They wait, silently.

The high hide.

Mommy's very angry.

They dangle, moments away from certain death.

There's a jolt, the trailer's on the move. It's being pushed along the ground, Malcolm looks outside the window to see where they're going. "Oh, God. They're pushing us over the cliff!"

There's a jolt, the trailer's on the move. It's being pushed along the ground, Malcolm looks outside the window to see where they're going. "Oh, God. They're pushing us over the cliff!"

They crawl rapidly towards the front end of the trailer as the opposite end begins to slowly tip over the cliff.

The trailer begins to dip towards the crashing waves five hundred feet below. Nick has a firm grip at the top of the trailer while Sarah can only hold on to an air vent, objects fall all around and onto them. Below him Sarah, looking for a better grip, grabs the door of the refrigerator, the safety latch holds firm. Debris crashes into the window below, cracking the glass. The refrigerator pulls away from the wall, only the power cable keeps it from falling. Sarah is hanging there, helpless.

The safety catch finally gives and Sarah is showered by the contents. Sarah loses her grip and screams as she falls down the trailer and smashes into the window. The glass spiderwebs but holds firm – for now. She recovers from the fall and realises below her, beneath the cracking glass, is the long drop to the sea. Nick and Malcolm, hanging precariously, shout to her not to move. Sarah, her fear of heights realised as never before, slowly tries to pull herself to her hands and knees. The glass cracks loudly as Malcolm calls out for her to hang on. He begins to move as fast as he can towards Sarah, noticing the phone hanging from a light fitting, he calls for Nick to retrieve it.

Sarah moves carefully, trying to reach for the metal grating running along the wall of the trailer. Nick reaches for the phone – now only six inches away. Malcolm moves closer to Sarah. The glass is cracking more frequently, spreading rapidly as Sarah reaches for the grating. Nick reaches the phone and is about to grab it when the trailer shifts forward. The phone falls, it's all the glass below needed to completely shatter it. Sarah screams as she falls. Malcolm lunges and he's got her by the wrist. She hangs out of the window as the phone and all the other debris crash into the rocks below.

The two trailers are split 'L-shaped'. One resting on the edge of the cliff, it's corner in the branches of a tree, and the other pointing down to the sea and rocks. The two huge T-rexes

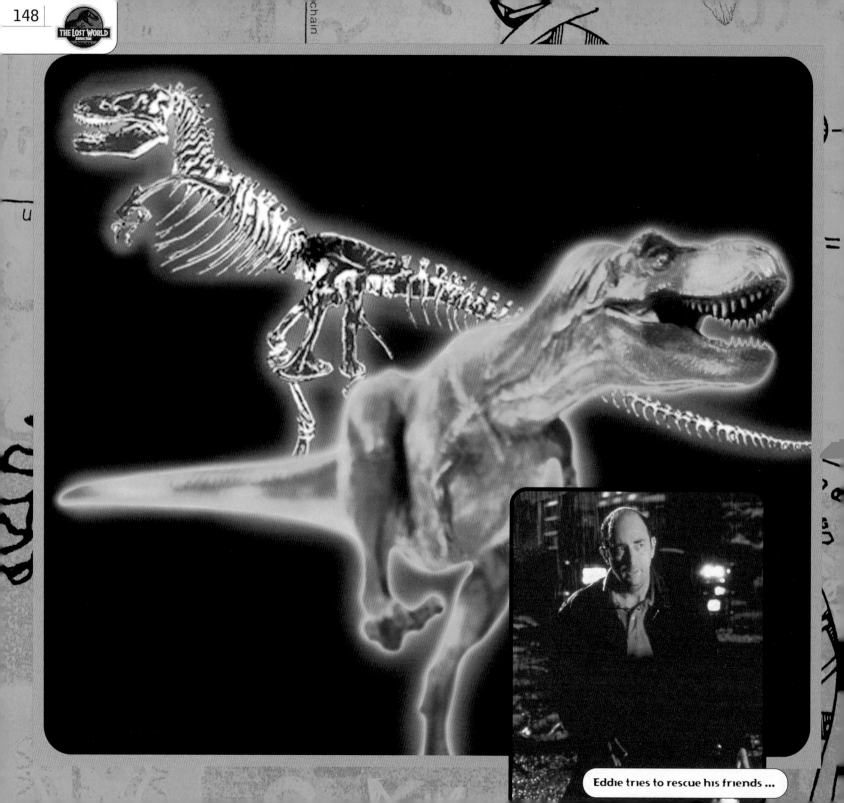

Eddie tries to rescue his friends ...

Above the noise of the roaring motor, Eddie doesn't hear another roar. But in the side view mirror he sees the T-rex crashing towards him and then the other one running alongside.

decide to turn and head back into the jungle. Sarah reaches up with her free hand and grips the metal grating and Malcolm pulls her back into the trailer. Nick moves down, joining Sarah and Malcolm. They move upwards, the tree branches begin to snap, the trailer moves downwards again – the connecting bellows between the two trailers are now at full stretch. Outside it's now raining heavily as Eddie drives the AAV, towards the trailers praying for them to hang on.

Eddie shouts into the trailer for any signs of life. Malcolm yells for him to get some rope, he asks them if they need anything else – and receives an order for three double cheeseburgers, one with no onions and an apple turnover from the relieved trio. Eddie runs back to the AAV, secures rope around a tree and runs back to the trailer which shifts again – then stops, causing panic once more. He crawls through the top trailer, hangs over the connecting bellows and throws the rope down. Eddie, slipping and sliding in the mud, is outside now running towards the power winch on the AAV's front as the trailer again moves closer towards the edge of the cliff. He stretches the cable and runs towards the trailer's towing hook. He's short by six inches.

They begin to climb up the rope. There's too much weight and the rope whirls from the tree and the three go crashing down and just manage to hold on, as their legs shoot through the broken window, to the edge of the frame.

Eddie has now managed to hook the cable to the trailer and secure the rope again. Eddie guns the gas and the tires spin helplessly in the mud. They begin to grip and the jeep shoots forward, the trailer begins to move back up to the cliff top as Malcolm, Sarah and Nick climb inside and grip the now secured rope. Above the noise of the roaring motor, Eddie doesn't hear another roar. But in the side view mirror he sees the T-rex crashing towards him and then the other one running alongside. The first bites the roof of the car off exposing a terrified Eddie. The gas pedal pops up which makes the jeep move forward and the trailer pitch over the side of the cliff. The rex stomps down on the moving AAV and stops it

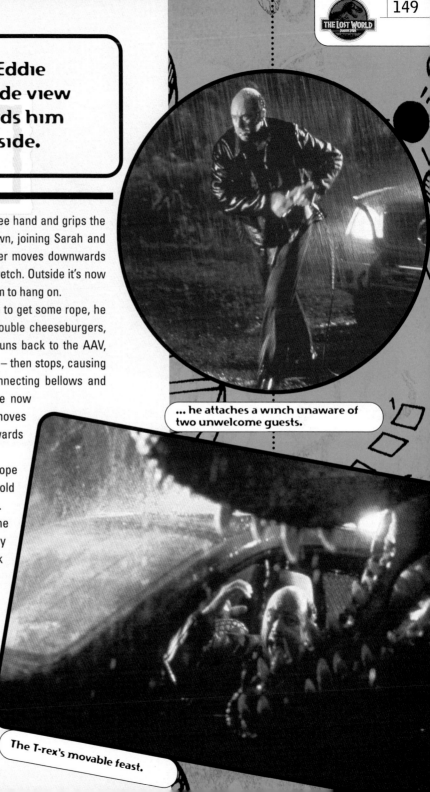

... he attaches a winch unaware of two unwelcome guests.

The T-rex's movable feast.

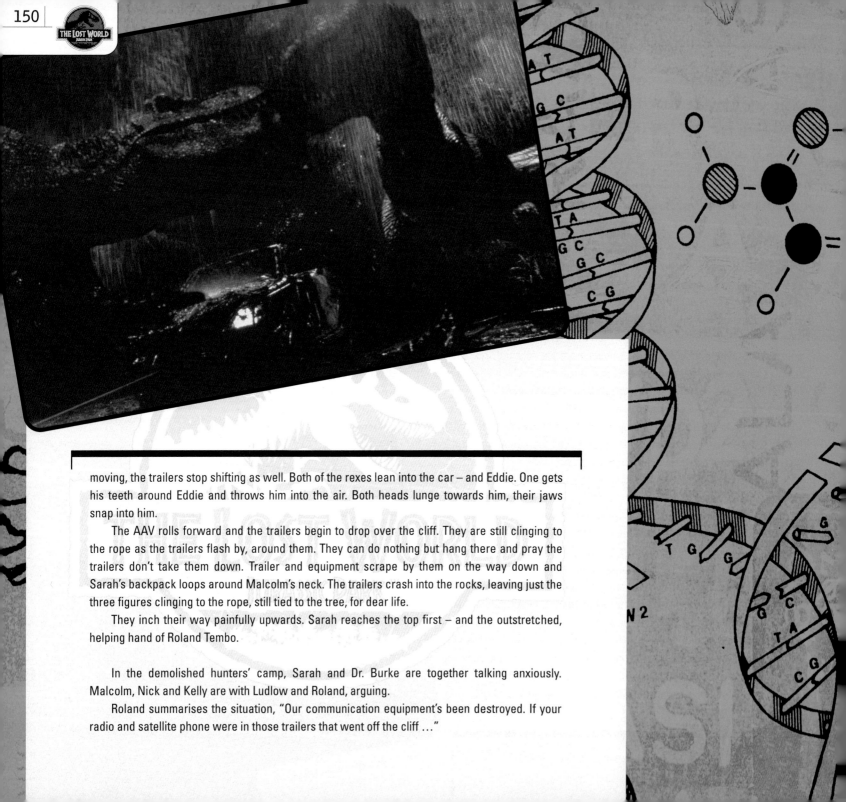

moving, the trailers stop shifting as well. Both of the rexes lean into the car – and Eddie. One gets his teeth around Eddie and throws him into the air. Both heads lunge towards him, their jaws snap into him.

The AAV rolls forward and the trailers begin to drop over the cliff. They are still clinging to the rope as the trailers flash by, around them. They can do nothing but hang there and pray the trailers don't take them down. Trailer and equipment scrape by them on the way down and Sarah's backpack loops around Malcolm's neck. The trailers crash into the rocks, leaving just the three figures clinging to the rope, still tied to the tree, for dear life.

They inch their way painfully upwards. Sarah reaches the top first – and the outstretched, helping hand of Roland Tembo.

In the demolished hunters' camp, Sarah and Dr. Burke are together talking anxiously. Malcolm, Nick and Kelly are with Ludlow and Roland, arguing.

Roland summarises the situation, "Our communication equipment's been destroyed. If your radio and satellite phone were in those trailers that went off the cliff …"

"They were," Malcolm confirms.

"Then we're stuck here, ladies and gentlemen – and stuck together. Thanks to you people," Roland tells them.

"Hey, we came here to observe, you came to strip-mine the place!" Nick shouts and then turns to Dieter who has been staring at him, "Back off."

"At least we came prepared. And until you intentionally destroyed all our ..." Ludlow is cut off by Malcolm.

"Prepared? Five years of work and a hundred miles of electrified fence couldn't prepare the other island, did you actually think a couple dozen Marlboro men would make a difference here?"

"It's a looter mentality. All you care about is what you can take. You have no right," Nick makes his point.

"An extinct animal that's brought back to life has no rights. It exists because we made it. We patented it. We own it," Ludlow barks back.

> "A day's walk, maybe more. That's not the problem," Ludlow answers.
> "What is?" asks Roland.
> "The velociraptors," Ludlow tells him.

Nick turns to Dieter, who continues to stare at him, "Are you looking for a problem?" he asks and lunges towards him, the others pulling them apart.

Roland turns to Nick, "I know you. You're that little Earth First bastard, aren't you?"

Sarah and Burke join the group as they argue about the merits of Earth First, telling them to keep their voices down.

"Listen to me, by moving the baby rex into our camps, we may have changed the adults' perceived territory!" Sarah tells them.

"That's why they persisted in destroying the trailers, they now feel they have to defend this entire area!" Dr. Burke explains and Sarah tells them they have to move – right now. Nick points out both their boat and the hunters' airlift are waiting for signals that they have no way to send.

Ludlow refers to some satellite photographs, "There's a communication centre, here in the old operations building. Hammond ran everything on geothermal power, it was never supposed to need replenishing. If we can get there, we can send a radio call for the airlift." Ludlow then answers Malcolm's question about having the radio frequency by lifting a small, leather log book. Roland grabs it from him and gives it to Ajay, who puts it in his backpack. Nick asks Ludlow how far the village is.

"A day's walk, maybe more. That's not the problem," Ludlow answers.

"What is?" asks Roland.

"The velociraptors," Ludlow tells him.

Ludlow continues that infrareds show the nesting sites are in the interior of the island. Dieter asks what velociraptors are and Burke gives him the deadly description. Burke and Sarah disagree when Sarah points out that the rexes may continue to track them, still fearing a threat to the infant.

Ludlow insists they should head for the village, Malcolm, having encountered velociraptors before, suggests the lagoon. The others point out that the captain of the boat is unlikely to return of his own accord. The village it is.

Their hopes for rescue are cruelly dashed.

SITE **B**

Planning for their escape.

The long trek to the workers' village.

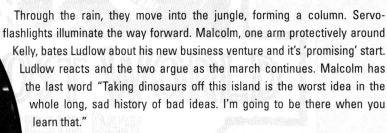

Through the rain, they move into the jungle, forming a column. Servo-flashlights illuminate the way forward. Malcolm, one arm protectively around Kelly, bates Ludlow about his new business venture and it's 'promising' start. Ludlow reacts and the two argue as the march continues. Malcolm has the last word "Taking dinosaurs off this island is the worst idea in the whole long, sad history of bad ideas. I'm going to be there when you learn that."

Further along Nick moves closer to Roland, who rolls his eyes when he sees him.

"Hey. You seem like you've got a shred of common sense. What are you doing here?" Nick asks him.

"Somewhere on this island, there exists the greatest predator that ever lived. And the second greatest predator must take him down," Roland replies as Nick looks at the gun slung over Roland's shoulder.

"You plan on using that?"

"Unless he surrenders."

"May I see that?" Nick reaches for the gun.

"Take that hand away," Roland eyes never even flicker.

"What's the matter with you? This animal exists on the planet for the first time in tens of millions of years, and the only way you can express yourself is to kill it?" Nick asks, exasperated.

"You remember that chap, about twenty years ago, forgot his name, but he climbed Everest without any oxygen, came down nearly dead. And they asked him, 'Why did you go up there, to die?' and he said 'I didn't. I went up there to live.' Yeah."

"The difference is the mountain got to live too," Nick mutters, knowing he's wasting his breath.

The march continues, heading down towards the interior of the island. It's daytime now, the rain has stopped and the marchers are exhausted. Roland calls for the party to rest and notices a few drops of blood on some foliage. Sarah sits by a tree and is joined by Roland, seeing Sarah's blood-stained shirt he asks if she's injured. She explains it's from the baby rex as Roland removes his elephant gun and rests it against the tree. Just as he's about to join it Ludlow calls him over to look at the satellite map. Nick sits down next to the rifle, he looks up at Roland in conversation with Ludlow and then back at the gun, deep in thought.

SITE B

Dieter Stark calls to his driver, Carter. They are resting well away from the others. He asks him to wait for him while he visits the 'ladies room,' toilet paper in hand he heads into the jungle. Carter sits with his back to his boss, his Walkman blasting out, headphones in position – he never even hears Dieter.

Dieter looks for a suitable clearing away from the thick growth. He finds one and is just about to unbuckle his belt when a strange noise catches his attention. Animal calls, small ones by the sounds, nothing to worry about. There's movement close by and his head whirls round to follow it. He moves forward and then he has his second sight of a compsognathus, just like the one that sniffed his boot and got a nasty shock earlier.

"It's not polite to sneak up on people," he tells the compy as the steel rod shoots out bolts of electricity into it's body. The wounded creature hurries away, whimpering into the jungle.

Dieter heads back to relieve himself, only he's not sure where he was when he left the trail. He goes a few paces one way and then another – nothing but the thick foliage around him. He calls out to Carter, but Carter has got the Walkman blasting out. None of the others are close enough to hear him.

Dieter hears the same movement again, from the other side. He's getting worried now, the noises are getting louder and closer, he gets his gun out. He crashes through the foliage, desperate to find the trail. He falls down, looks up and sees about forty compys surrounding him. He laughs nervously just before they shriek and rush him at the same time. They cover his body, teeth biting and claws ripping. Dieter is screaming and thrashing about, shaking

Tembo shows concern at the sight of blood on Sarah's jacket.

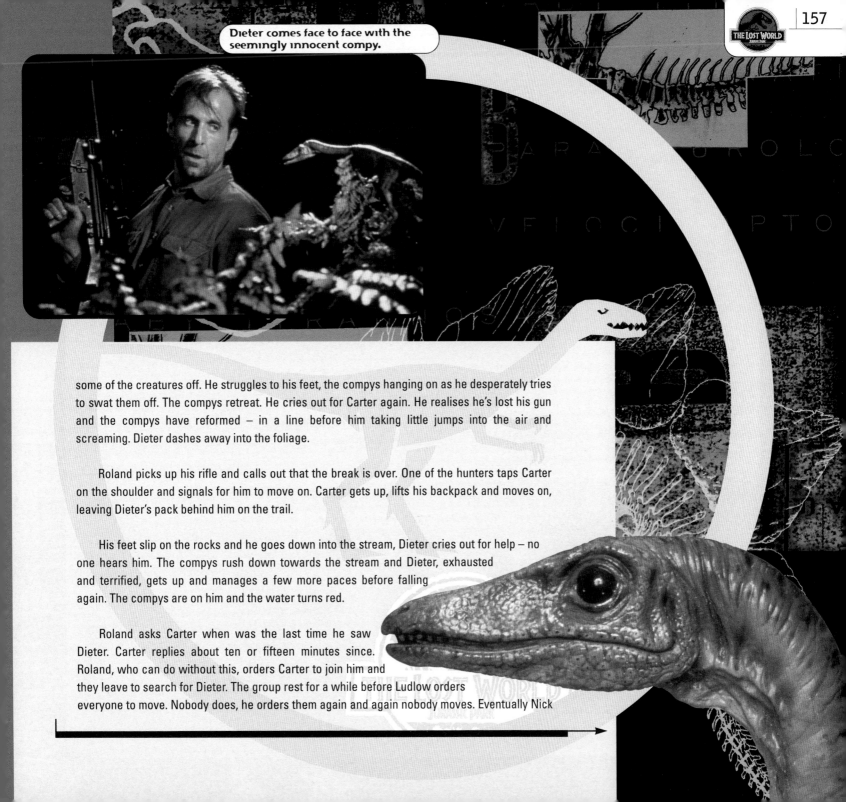

Dieter comes face to face with the seemingly innocent compy.

some of the creatures off. He struggles to his feet, the compys hanging on as he desperately tries to swat them off. The compys retreat. He cries out for Carter again. He realises he's lost his gun and the compys have reformed – in a line before him taking little jumps into the air and screaming. Dieter dashes away into the foliage.

Roland picks up his rifle and calls out that the break is over. One of the hunters taps Carter on the shoulder and signals for him to move on. Carter gets up, lifts his backpack and moves on, leaving Dieter's pack behind him on the trail.

His feet slip on the rocks and he goes down into the stream, Dieter cries out for help – no one hears him. The compys rush down towards the stream and Dieter, exhausted and terrified, gets up and manages a few more paces before falling again. The compys are on him and the water turns red.

Roland asks Carter when was the last time he saw Dieter. Carter replies about ten or fifteen minutes since. Roland, who can do without this, orders Carter to join him and they leave to search for Dieter. The group rest for a while before Ludlow orders everyone to move. Nobody does, he orders them again and again nobody moves. Eventually Nick

Roland and Carter enter the make-shift camp later that night. Ludlow asks Roland if they found Dieter.

"Only the bits they didn't like," he grimly replies.

shouts out that it's time to go, everyone gets up follows him, even Ludlow.

Roland and Carter enter the make-shift camp later that night. Ludlow asks Roland if they found Dieter.

"Only the bits they didn't like," he grimly replies.

Roland looks at the map and points out the operations building is a mile and a half Northwest from the base of the cliffs. He tells the exhausted marchers that the journey won't be easy. They'll sleep one more hour and then move on.

A small group of tents have been erected in the makeshift camp site. Nearly everyone sleeps soundly after their recent exertions. Roland Tembo rests up in a tree, close to the camp, keeping a watchful eye. Malcolm lies next to Kelly in one of the tents. He talks to her softly, reassuring her that he'll take care of her. Kelly suggest he marries Sarah, Malcolm points out that that's not what he meant. Sarah crawls into the tent and Kelly mischievously smiles. Malcolm kisses her on the head and tells them he'll be back, just taking one more look around the camp. Sarah hangs her shirt up in the tent.

Sarah and Kelly lay there drifting into sleep. Through the open flap the breeze causes the shirt to gently sway. Sarah looks up at it, her eyes begin to widen as she realises, for the first time, the danger from the blood on the shirt. The shirt begins to sway faster and the ground begins to vibrate.

Outside Malcolm stops, he's felt it. In the tree Roland sits up, he's felt it. Malcolm and Roland have now met up on the edge of the campsite, listening intently together. The noise has stopped. No it hasn't. It's moving in, faster.

The rex's massive head comes through the flap of the tent, sniffing loudly. Sarah is rigid with fear as the rex continues to sniff. Kelly wakes up and asks, "Who's that?" before Sarah clasps her hand over her mouth. The two lay there, hardly daring to breath. Suddenly it decides it can't find anything and it's head rears up, taking the tent with it.

Carter wakes first and spots the rex and screams, just as another rex stomps into the camp. The camp erupts in full panic, men running in all directions. Malcolm screams for them not to run.

The compys reek their revenge.

For Dieter there's no escape.

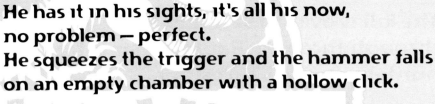

He has it in his sights, it's all his now,
no problem — perfect.
He squeezes the trigger and the hammer falls
on an empty chamber with a hollow click.

Roland lifts the elephant gun and tries to get a shot. He has it in his sights, it's all his now, no problem — perfect. He squeezes the trigger and the hammer falls on an empty chamber with a hollow click. He can't believe it, breaking open both barrels he stares into the two vacant chambers.

Malcolm runs into the fleeing hunters towards Kelly and Sarah, both are still on the ground, scrambling out of the sleeping bags. Malcolm is knocked to the ground in the rush to escape by the oncoming hunters. Nick rushes over and helps Kelly and Sarah up and all three run into the jungle, just as the second rex bursts onto the scene causing the fleeing hunters to run down a narrow ravine, the second rex follows them.

Roland has scrambled across to a large metal box. Inside there are three tranquilliser rifles. The first T-rex looks at Roland with serious intent. Roland fumbles to load one of the cartridges, full of concentrated nerve agents, into the gun. The rex, forty yards away, charges.

Roland snaps the gun shut and takes aim as the rex thunders towards him. It stops ten yards away and roars into Roland's face. Roland squeezes the trigger and prays, "Please God — work fast," as the animal prepares to charge again.

Some of the hunters, now the prey, have tried to scale the rocks unsuccessfully. Carter goes down and a huge foot tramples him. Carter is carried along, stuck to the rex's sole, before being crushed into the ground.

Nick spots the waterfall, something not quite right about, yells at Sarah and Kelly and grabs them. They leap forward towards the waterfall, Sarah and Kelly thinking they're going to smash into the rocks but trusting Nick in this desperate situation. They find themselves in a small cave, just big enough for the three of them to hide behind the water. They're frightened, but feeling safer. Until Dr. Burke follows them yelling at the trio to move out of the way, he pushes against the far wall. The huge tyrannosaur head shoots

From the jungle Malcolm hears a terrifying sound.

The kill is over in seconds. Panic spreads through the field. Raptors tear after the hunters, there is no escape.

through the water, Burke's given the hiding place away. The massive head is too large to fit in the opening, the jaws snap onto fresh air as the four scream and panic. The rex, frustrated shoots it's tongue out hoping to wrap it around one of it's prey. Burke pushes himself further into the cave, but in doing so pushes Kelly out. Sarah screams at him to stop it. Burke doesn't listen, he just burrows in further dislodging something that looks like a cross between a snake and a centipede, it crawls down his shirt. Screaming he leaps towards the water. The rex's tongue swiftly wraps round him before he's hardly moved and Burke is pulled into the rex's mouth. The water in front of the others turns into a screen of red. The rex carries Burke away. They breathe a sigh of relief until Nick hears something outside and whispers to the others that it's coming back. Malcolm jumps into the cave and they all heave another sigh of relief.

The hunters have reached the end of the ravine, they tear into the long 'elephant' grass, still in panic. Ajay stops and yells to them not to go into the grass – he is totally ignored. He races after them, shouting at them to stop. The hunters are far into the grass when they realise they are no longer being pursued. Ajay calls for them to come back – but they think they're safe. They don't notice the three heads rising, looking and descending back into the grass. The hunters continue, behind them four more heads rise and descend. To both sides of them the long grass begins to ripple. One of the hunters at the back suddenly goes down, no one notices. Then another, and another. The fourth victim hears the noise behind him and turns just in time to see

the velociraptor lunge forward, it's curved claw, a 'killing-claw', extended and ready to slash it's victim. The kill is over in seconds. Panic spreads through the field. Raptors tear after the hunters, there is no escape. Ajay looks around, he's gone too far in. Four trails move towards him – he closes his eyes, it's all over.

THE LOST WORLD

The awesome T-rex pursues its prey.

Carter's grizzly fate.

The grass begins to shiver. Malcolm freezes and then snaps out of it, "Go! Go! As fast as you can! Go!" The velociraptor shoots up, Ajay's blood dripping from it's jaws.

Malcolm, Kelly, Nick and Sarah reach the edge of the elephant grass. They have no idea of the danger within. They walk in until Nick stumbles across something – he's found Ajay's pack. The grass begins to shiver. Malcolm freezes and then snaps out of it, "Go! Go! As fast as you can! Go!" The velociraptor shoots up, Ajay's blood dripping from it's jaws. They run as fast as they can, other raptors now join in the hunt, gaining ground. They're not going to make it, the grass suddenly stops and the four find themselves rolling down the side of a steep hill, crashing through the foliage, unable to stop if they wanted to. They land at the bottom with a thud. All but Malcolm get to their feet. They look up – the raptors haven't followed. Malcolm has landed awkwardly, once again damaging his bad leg. Nick helps him up, he's clearly in pain.

The pain is momentarily forgotten as Malcolm looks amazed at the area in front of them. And at the vast number of dinosaur skeletons of all sizes, from the smallest to the largest. Many different species litter the graveyard. Malcolm looks further ahead and points into the far distance. What remains of the worker village can be seen in the moonlight.

"They said the communication centre's in the operations building. I'll get in there and send the radio call. See you there!" Nick tears off towards through the graveyard to the building. The others follow, Malcolm limping badly.

Nick reaches Isla Sorna's worker village or what's left of it. The hurricane has left derelict stores, cafes, houses, gas station and at the far end, the large four storey building that is the communications centre. Everything's a total mess and the jungle has started to reclaim the area. Nick enters the large building and finds the communications room almost at once. He turns the power on and goes to the sophisticated radio console and flips the relevant switches, his heart beating rapidly. It crackles to life, a couple of bulbs burst but everything else seems fine. He pulls the log book from Ajay's pack and calls for help.

...mbo moves in for the kill.

At the destroyed, makeshift campsite something stirs beneath an abandoned canvas. Peter Ludlow emerges from his hiding place. He looks at the scene of destruction all around him and then he smiles, wide-eyed and smiling an even bigger smile.

Malcolm, Sarah and Kelly have at last made it to the village. From the communications room they can see the light. Delighted they move towards the building just as the velociraptor leaps onto the old abandoned truck. Then another one joins it and a third comes round the side. Stunned, and frozen rigid they are unable to move until one of the velociraptors leaps onto Sarah. She crashes into the others, knocking them down. The raptor's teeth sink into her lucky backpack, it's head jerks it to one side, ripping the pack of her. Sarah rolls away as the raptor rips the backpack to shreds. She looks up to see the second raptor rushing towards her, it joins the other to feed off 'the kill'. The three struggle to their feet and make for a tall, corrugated metal building. Sarah gets there first. Malcolm, holding Kelly behind him, stops as the raptor stands yards away and looks him in the face. He shoves Kelly towards Sarah, screaming at her to run. Malcolm picks up a piece of old iron bar and runs to a long abandoned jeep, hitting it with the bar and shouting at the raptor who turns it's attention away from the fleeing Kelly towards Malcolm. He looks behind him to see Kelly dart through the door.

Malcolm takes off into the gas station building. The raptor, hot on his heels, crashes into the closed door. The large, plate-glass window at the side of the door shatters as the raptor leaps to

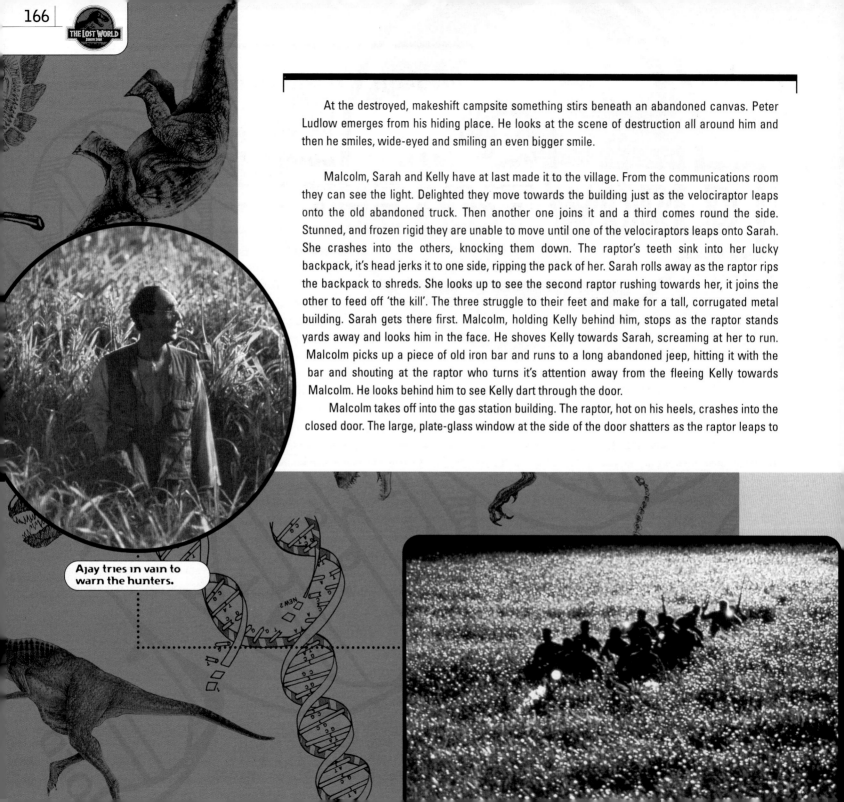

Ajay tries in vain to warn the hunters.

VELOCIRAPTOR TERRITORY

> **They move further into the long grass.**

the ledge, head inside, tail hanging outside, looking for Malcolm. Malcolm shoots back through the door as the raptor enters the gas station but the raptor leaps back cutting Malcolm off. He hides behind the open door as the raptor leaps to the window frame again. Whichever way Malcolm runs, into the gas station or out of it, the raptor's got him, if it can wait. Malcolm rips the rotting door from it's hinges and holds it in front of him as a shield – the raptor leaps, smashing into the glass and sending Malcolm crashing through the window and out into the street. He rolls over and runs to the old jeep, slamming the door behind him. The raptor leaps onto the front of the vehicle and starts smashing it's head into the windscreen, the perspex glass begins to crack as blow after blow reigns down upon it. Malcolm realises it's only a matter of time before the raptor's head gets to him, opens the door and makes a run for it.

Sarah and Kelly have taken refuge in a three story kiln house, used for pottery and other projects. A wooden building with a floor of earth. Above them scaffolding and chain-lined catwalks dominate the windowless building.

They wonder what to do next when they hear the burrowing sound from the other side of the door. One of the raptor's trying to tunnel in. They run to the opposite wall and feverishly begin to dig with their bare hands, the earth flying out as the sound of the raptor's digging and snorting become louder. Sarah pulls at the bottom of one of the planks and yanks it off to give them more

With deadly precision the raptors move in.

Sarah urges Kelly to hurry and she begins to crawl through the space just as the third snorting, raptor's head appears right in front of her face.

digging room, they've got a space of about eighteen inches now – just enough to get through. Sarah urges Kelly to hurry and she begins to crawl through the space just as the third snorting, raptor's head appears right in front of her face.

There's a loud, piercing scream as Kelly is dragged back by Sarah. Sarah looks up at the scaffolding above.

"Can you climb this stuff?" Sarah asks Kelly. Kelly answers her by leaping onto one of the catwalks with grace and ease.

"Yeah, I guess you can," says Sarah and begins the climb, her fear of heights overcome by the raptor's furious digging. They're halfway up the scaffolding, moving from catwalk to catwalk, when Malcolm throws open the corrugated metal door and comes in, shouting Kelly's name. Kelly and Sarah call to him and Malcolm begins to climb, his feet barely off the floor as the raptor's head appears under the wall. Malcolm curses and moves faster. The wall splinters as more of the raptor appears.

Kelly has nearly reached the top of the scaffolding now and moves onto a ledge below the roofline and into the open. She reaches down to help pull Sarah up, calling for her father to hurry up. The raptor leaps into the scaffolding and Malcolm begins to slip, shaken by the impact. The raptor's climbing towards him as Malcolm falls, past the raptor and onto a maze of bars only six feet below the raptor. The raptor crouches and prepares to jump at the fallen Malcolm.

Kelly leaps from the top and swings from a bar, the raptor springs towards her father as Kelly shoots down, feet first into the raptor and knocks it off balance and it crashes through the wall, landing on sharp, rusty pipes amid machinery outside, screaming in agony as the sharp metal spears

through it's body. Kelly lands next to Malcolm and they untangle themselves and take the short steps back to the ground.

"And they cut you from the team?" Malcolm remarks to Kelly about her life-saving gymnastics.

"You're safer up there! Take the rooftops, just get the helicopter!" Malcolm shouts up to Sarah just as the second raptor comes out of the hole in the wall and spots Sarah up above. It leaps onto the scaffolding and begins to climb with amazing speed. Malcolm and Kelly race to the door, slamming it shut as they go outside.

Sarah kicks the window of the slanted kiln roof through and climbs onto the roof outside. The helicopter is only a few buildings away. Sarah jumps to the roof of the next building between two sides of the sloping roof and gets to her feet. Behind her the raptor has made it to the roof of the kiln house and suddenly it flies through the air. And lands right in front of Sarah. She crawls down the sloping roof as the Spanish tiles begin to give way. Sarah hangs onto the slippery ceramic tiles as they slowly begin to shift downwards. Sarah looks over her shoulder to the roof below. The other remaining raptor is there, waiting for her. She swiftly rolls away and the sliding section of the roof crashes into the raptor's head. Sarah is now clinging desperately to the roof

A trio of pure evil ...

tiles and suddenly, they give one more time and she hurtles downwards towards the waiting raptor. She manages to get hold of the gutter and hangs there, helplessly. One raptor below her, the other above.

One moves down towards her and the other leaps up, jaws snapping at her dangling legs. She lifts her legs up but is quickly realising this can't go on for much longer. She pulls a tile from the roof and throws it down, hitting the raptor in the head. It does little good but it's all she's got left. She desperately throws more and more as quick as she can. But the one above is almost on her. She pulls more and more tiles free, noticing the whole section is beginning to come loose under the raptor's feet. The loose tiles break free under the weight of the raptor and there's a quick, short avalanche – tiles and raptor fall from the roof, missing Sarah by inches. The raptor crashes into the one below. Angrily the animals begin to fight as Sarah loses her grip and falls next to the snarling antagonists. The animals roll over, Sarah rolls out of the way and falls through a hole in the roof. She lands on top of a old-fashioned hanging fluorescent light fixture. One end immediately snaps away from the roof and Sarah slides down, smashes through a window and lands in the muddy street below. She jerks as she's grabbed from behind – it's Malcolm.

He lifts her to her feet and the two join the waiting Kelly as the helicopter's searchlight beams on them. They make it to the main building and shut the heavy door behind them, exhausted and relieved.

They join Nick on the roof and prepare to board the helicopter. One of the InGen workers tells Malcolm that another helicopter is looking for more survivors. As the helicopter takes off Malcolm drapes both arms around Sarah and Kelly, who cries and whimpers softly against her father's shoulder. He comforts her. Nick is sat opposite and reaches into his pocket. Two long bullets rest in the palm of his hand.

"There's one souvenir they won't be taking with them," Nick muses as he looks at Roland Tembo's ammunition.

Sarah looks out of the window at the island below and sits up with a jolt, "Oh, my God, no!" The others press against the windows and are dumbstruck by the sight before their eyes as they pass over the ruined campsite. They see bright worklights illuminating busy InGen workers and two helicopters circling close to the ground. And they see the giant tyrannosaurus rex, laying on it's side, tranquillised – no wonder Peter Ludlow was smiling as he crawled out from his hiding place earlier. They see the harness being lowered from the helicopter to lift the animal and carry it away. A huge barge can be seen moving close to the shore – the barge is designed to transport heavy cargo.

"We've lost," Nick mutters.

Below Ludlow shouts orders to the InGen workers. The tranquillised T-rex is ready to be lifted.

"Find the infant tyrannosaur, Roland can tell you where the nest is! I want it on the jet with me, I'll take it directly to the infirmary at the complex in San Diego! Move it, we have to be airborne before the female knows we're here!" Ludlow moves over to a strangely subdued Roland. "You probably saved InGen. We lost everything we came after on this trip, but that rex and it's infant are going to single-handedly bail us out."

"Congratulations," Roland, half-heartedly, remarks.

"You've got your trophy. But it's alive, and everyone on the planet's going to line up to appreciate it and what you've done for us." He notices Roland's lack of enthusiasm, "What's the matter?"

"Ajay. He didn't make it."

"I'm sorry. Really, I am. I remember the people who help me, Roland. There's a job for you at the park in San Diego, if you want it."

Roland shakes his head, "No. Not for me. I believe I have spent enough time in the company of death."

The abandoned workers' villa[ge]

SITE B
INGEN OPERATIONS/ZONE 4

They prepare for what seems like the end of their ordeal.

To chain

They arrive at the village.

The raptors arrive as well.

San Diego

Peter Ludlow addresses the executives and stockholders of InGen late at night at the waterfront complex. It is a scene of great activity, lights illuminate the whole area, a large flatbed truck with a huge cage, sits between two towering cranes, ready to take a heavy load. The cage is well lit and tranquilliser guns, pointing at the cage, are fitted in specially designed ports. Dock handlers, loaders, crane operators and security guards crowd the dock area. A thick mist hangs over the sea.

"Well, half an hour from now, John Hammond's dream, re-imagined, will come true. For one-hundredth the cost of building a destination resort thousands of miles away, tonight we'll christen 'Jurassic Park, San Diego' with a mega-attraction that's going to drive turnstile numbers to rival any theme park in the world. I want to thank each one of you for being intrepid enough to turn up at three in the morning to …" Ludlow is interrupted by the gesticulations of the harbour master, trying to get his attention, "Excuse me," Ludlow moves to one side as the harbour master whispers to him, telling him the ship is here. "It's early?" Ludlow asks.

"It's … you'd better come look," the harbour master replies. Ludlow makes a 'won't be long' gesture and follows the harbour master towards his office.

Ludlow sees Sarah and Malcolm get out of a car outside the security fence. A guard refuses to let them through until Ludlow intervenes, telling the guard that he has invited them.

"The loyal opposition. Come on in. I was hoping you'd want to see this," Ludlow gleefully tells the couple as the harbour master hurries him inside. The harbour master gets behind his console and refers to the radar screen.

"Look, that's their transponder signal, 'Venture 5888'. They're headed into port, but I can't raise them," he grimly informs Ludlow who urges him to try again. Outside the faint noise of the ship's engines can just be heard.

"Skipper SS Venture, this is InGen Harbour Master, do you copy, over?" Everyone looks out of the window through the fog, now much denser than it was earlier. The noise of the engines throb louder and louder.

"Skipper SS Venture, you are approaching the breakwater at flank speed, reduce at once! Over." The harbour master is even more worried now, muffled breaking sounds can be heard through the fog and the crowd on the dock are becoming concerned.

"SS Venture, this is InGen Harbour Master, you are entering a docking area at twenty-six knots, make your engines full reverse, repeat, you are entering …" the SS Venture bursts through the fog and towards the loading dock.

The crowd panic and stampede as the ship crashes into the dock with no signs of slowing

down. Everyone bolts from the harbour master's office and take refuge as best they can. The ship, leaving destroyed boats in it's wake, heads for the InGen port, demolishing the pier on it's way. A transformer is struck and the arc lights go out leaving the dock in semi-darkness. It continues through the harbour master's shack, demolishes the cranes, the flatbed with the cage and anything else that happens to be in it's way and eventually comes to a halt with dull thud and a pained groan.

People, shaken by the experience, begin to come out of wherever they have been hiding and stare at the huge ship as it gently rocks to and fro. Two security guards, flashlights in hand, board the ship. Whatever it is that they see, it causes them stop dead in their tracks, horror spreads across their faces. Malcolm, Sarah and Ludlow climb up, others follow them, Ludlow shouting at the guard.

"What the hell happened?! Where's the crew?!"

"All over the place," the guard replies.

They move through the blood and what could be flesh, that cover the deck. The harness that was used to lift the T-rex lays before them – destroyed.

"We've got to get off this boat!" Malcolm fearfully states.

"What in God's name have you done?" Sarah, bewildered, asks Ludlow.

"We've got to get off this boat right now!" Malcolm reiterates.

"Check the cargo hold! Maybe the crew's hiding down there!" Ludlow shouts.

INGEN PRODUCTION
12/16/00
DX
TAG AND RELEASE

SITE B

VELOCIRAPTOR
WARM BLOODED
HIGHLY AGGRESSIVE
HIGHLY INTELLIGENT

SPECIES NUMBER
RAP-GAAT
GA212629
CARNIVORE
TM & © UCS & AMBLIN

A raptor pounces on Sarah.

The two huge steel doors that are built into the deck covering the hold below are half-open, joining in the middle, like a tent. The strain of a motor can be heard, trying to fully open the doors. Malcolm moves to a electric panel where the door mechanism is controlled from. The hand of a dead member of the crew rests on it. Startled, he turns and shouts to the two guards who approaching the doors.

"No! Get away from the ...", the doors fly violently back, sending the guards skittling sideways, a loud roar vibrates beneath them and everyone moves back. The once sedated tyrannosaur shoots through the opening and lands on the deck before the horrified onlookers. They scatter everywhere, taking refuge wherever they can find it. The rex bolts across the deck and leaps into the air and onto the docks.

Malcolm, Sarah and Ludlow watch from the boat as the T-rex thunders along, demolishing the security fence as if it were made of paper. It moves towards a second security fence flattening anything that gets in it's way.

"Now you're John Hammond," a disgusted Malcolm tells Ludlow.

The second security fence offers no resistance as the T-rex walks through it with ease. The sign that reads 'Welcome to the United States of America. No Fruits, Vegetables Or Animals Beyond This Point' clatters to the ground as the T-rex walks

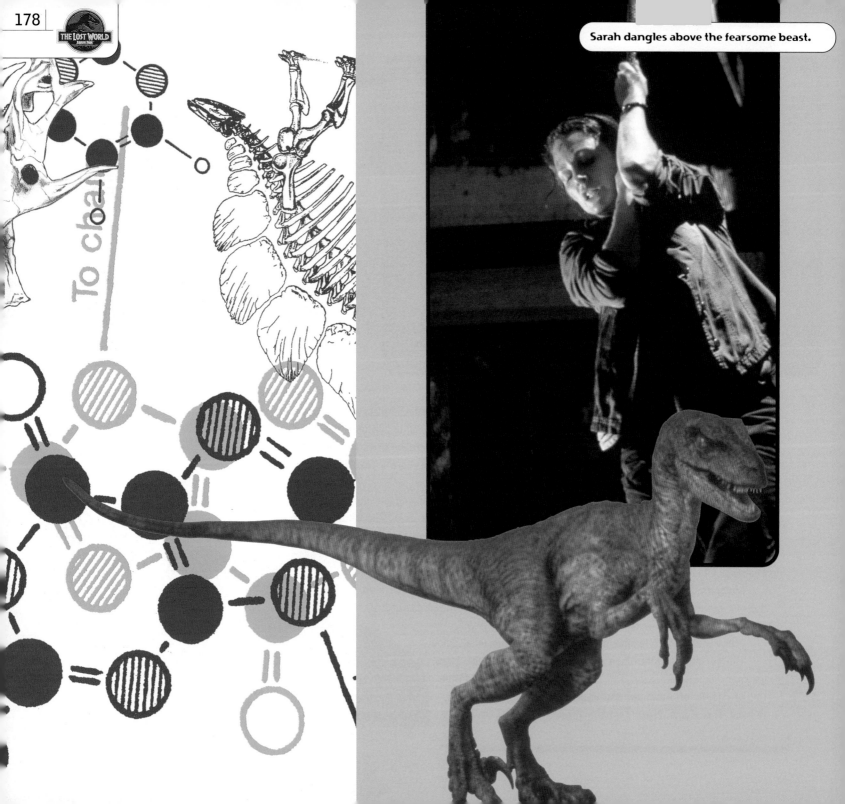

Sarah dangles above the fearsome beast.

> ## "When we brought the baby to the trailers it came, didn't it? There's no reason to think it wouldn't follow it here."

straight through it. The T-rex stomps on as the bright lights of the city beckon in the distance.

The dock is being evacuated with all speed. People driving or running away from the scene of pandemonium. Ludlow, stunned, his dreams shattered, stares blankly.

"Why the hell wasn't it tranquillised?" Sarah turns to an InGen employee, she recognises from the island.

"It was! Roland hit it with two darts of concentrated Carfentanil, over ten milligrams," the man replies.

"Ten milligrams? That should have put it into a coma!" Sarah can't believe it.

"It stopped breathing, so we gave it Naltrexone to counteract the effects. We didn't know how much to use, we didn't plan on tranquillising the rexes at all, so we hadn't run any body weight calculations," the man explains.

"You administered an antagonist without knowing the proper dosage? You put the animal in a narcoleptic state – that thing's a locomotive now! And it's dehydrated, it'll look for a water source."

Malcolm asks the InGen man if there were any other animals on the ship.

"No. We brought the infant back on the plane."

Ludlow stares blankly out into the open sea, financial ruin and disgrace staring him in the face. Sarah turns to Ludlow "You have the infant?"

"Yes, but it's safe," Ludlow answers.

Sarah turns to Malcolm, an idea spreading across her face as she explains that they must get the animal back to the dock because when it drinks it's going to find the next thing it's body needs. If they can get it back to the dock there's still enough containment equipment left and the ship still looks seaworthy. Malcolm nods in agreement but wonders how they can get the rex to come back to the dock.

"When we brought the baby to the trailers it came, didn't it? There's no reason to think it wouldn't follow it here," Sarah answers.

Kelly and Sarah warn Malcolm.

Sarah turns to Ludlow and asks where the infant is, he tells them in the amphitheatre, Malcolm asks him exactly where and he tells them. Malcolm and Sarah tear towards their car.

Toy dinosaurs sit on the shelves of Benjamin's bedroom. The water in the goldfish tank begins to circle as the vibration gets stronger. Benjamin opens his eyes and sits up in bed, concerned. He calls out for this Daddy, there's no reply. He gets out of bed as a dog barks in the street outside and he walks to the window and starts to close the drapes. The dinosaur's head passes by the bedroom window.

Ben goes rigid for a moment, not quite believing what he's just seen. He peers out of the window again as the tyrannosaur moves to the families' swimming pool. The dog strains on it's chain and stands outside it's kennel, barking loudly at the dinosaur, now drinking huge gulps of water from the pool. The T-rex looks around at the annoying dog and then bends down and lifts both the kennel and the dog into it's mouth.

Benjamin has run into his parents bedroom, frantically trying to wake

Fleeing to an abandoned car

them up, "There's a dinosaur in our back yard!" Sleepily they follow him to the window, the kid's obviously having a bad dream, and look out. They see the T-rex chewing whatever's left of the dog, the chain hanging out of the dinosaur's mouth and the kennel falling to the ground. Benjamin's mother lets out a terrifying scream and the family move quickly backwards. The rex hears the scream and lumbers over to the house. The terrified family stare at the massive head, it's huge eye looking at them only a few feet away. Ben clicks the shutter down, the camera flashes and the head of the startled tyrannosaur smashes through the wall, sniffs loudly and moves away, leaving the shaking family to recover. Benjamin can't resist one last look through the window as the rex strolls through the neighbour's back yards, trampling anything that's in it's path.

Sarah's grip loosens.

The car crashes through the security barriers as the guards leap to one side. In the nearly finished InGen amphitheatre, situated in the complex, a row of cages are empty except for one. The baby tyrannosaur sleeps on a bed of straw. Sarah examines the eyes and concludes that the animal is heavily sedated. Malcolm and Sarah carry it to the car, as security guards approach, guns at the ready.

She leaps to 'freedom'.

"How are we going to find the adult?"
Sarah asks.
"Follow the screams," Malcolm
replies.

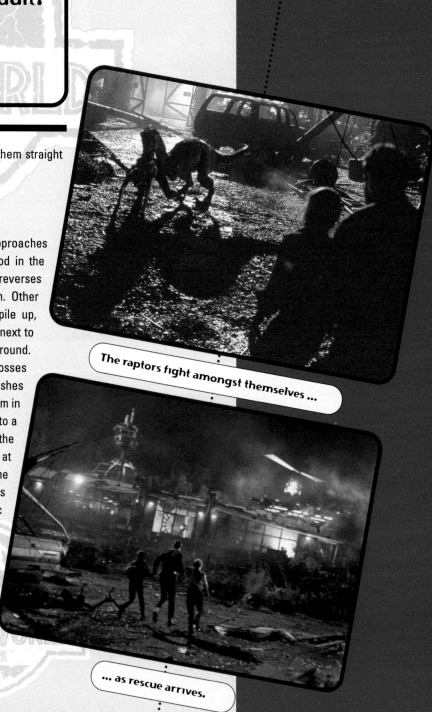

The raptors fight amongst themselves ...

... as rescue arrives.

"If you really want to stop us, shoot us," Malcolm tells them straight and guns the car away from the stunned security guards.

"How are we going to find the adult?" Sarah asks.

"Follow the screams," Malcolm replies.

The woman screams and slams her brakes on as she approaches the four way intersection – and the tyrannosaurus rex stood in the middle of it. The rex looks and roars towards her. The woman reverses the car into another one heading towards the intersection. Other cars, avoiding the rex, slam into them and cars begin to pile up, terrified drivers run for their lives. The rex bites the stoplight next to it's head and rips the pole and the power cables from the ground. The electric sparks fly and crackle and sting the rex who tosses the pole to one side. A bus comes round the corner and crashes into the rex. It's head swings down low and passengers scream in terror as the head knocks the bus spinning across the road into a store. From the night-club opposite, people flood out onto the street wondering what the hell's going on. The rex looks at them, fair game, and roars. They flee down the street, some looking behind them, see the rex has disappeared. It appears from between two tall buildings – in front of them. They panic again and scatter. One poor unfortunate man hesitates, not sure which way to run, he doesn't have time to make up his mind as the rex scoops him and smashes him down to the ground. It's just about to eat him when it's head moves to one side, sniffing at something in the air. It's got the scent of something and cranes it's head to look around the now deserted street.

SITE
B

Sarah looks down on a terrifying sight.

Ludlow briefs the press on his deadly cargo.

"Tell them to shoot it, you understand, shoot the adult — but get the baby back alive!"

The car drives close by, they are unaware of the destruction at the intersection. Malcolm driving, Sarah in the back with the sedated baby T-rex. Malcolm shouts at Sarah to make the baby cry so the adult can hear it. She tries but the baby sleeps soundly as the car approaches the intersection. Sarah sees it first, stood almost proudly amidst the damage at the intersection. Malcolm slams his foot down and the car skids – towards the rex. The car does a full circle and Sarah finds herself heading towards the rex's open jaws. Malcolm releases the brake and hits the gas, and the car screams away as the jaws snap shut on nothing but the night air.

Malcolm accelerates towards the waterfront as the T-rex thunders after them, crashing through a billboard on the way. Three police cars, lights flashing and sirens sounding, scream in front of the car. Malcolm swerves and crashes into the sidewalk, sending garbage cans flying. He pulls back onto the road but the detour has allowed the rex to gain valuable ground, it's closing in, fast. Malcolm swerves to the right and six police cars come round the corner. The rex stops it's foot down in front of them and all six cars stop dead, reverse round and flee the opposite way. Sarah shouts at Malcolm asking him if he knows a short cut to the harbour. He swings the wheel and the car crashes through the wooden wall of a empty warehouse and goes through a partitioned office, skidding across the floor and stopping at the opposite side. Steam rises from the crumpled front end. Malcolm and Sarah grab the baby and make for the opening just as the rex crashes through the flimsy wall and into the warehouse, it's head swinging round as it searches for them. They make a run for it, heading out of the back door and towards the boat in the harbour.

At the now deserted InGen dock, Peter Ludlow shouts into a cellular phone, "Tell them to shoot it, you understand, shoot the adult – but get the baby back alive! Find Malcolm and Harding and …" he breaks off as he sees Malcolm and Sarah, the baby in their arms climbing the ladder of the ship.

Ludlow races after them and starts to climb the ladder. He has only one thing on his mind – getting the infant back. As he reaches the deck Malcolm and Sarah jump into the water.

"Hey! What did you do with it?! They've got the adult cornered and I want that infant, do you hear me?!" he screams at the two swimmers and then he hears the crying baby dinosaur, "Thank God."

Ludlow descends into the hold and climbs down. Ludlow talks to the infant, trying to get the muzzle he's found back on it's jaws. it struggles and cries. The thud on the deck rocks the boat and Ludlow almost tipples over. He regains his balance and looks up as the tyrannosaur's huge massive head comes into view. The baby calls out and the adult coos back. Ludlow is frozen, unable to move. He then carefully places the baby on the floor and steps back. The rex jumps down into the hold and simply stares at him as if it were coming to a decision. The huge head comes down and nudges Ludlow, he crashes to the floor, his eyes showing pure, naked terror. The rex now gently nudges the infant – towards Ludlow. The baby knows exactly what's going on and gets to it's feet, unsteadily it walks towards Ludlow. He begins to run, but the adult nudges him down again and then lifts it's head to watch. Ludlow makes another run for it and is brought down again. This time he crawls away on all fours. The jaws of the adult rex grip Ludlow's leg and bite through the bone. Ludlow screams in agony. The baby toddles over and jumps onto his chest, looks at him and it's jaws open. That's the last thing Peter Ludlow ever saw.

Malcolm tries to get Ludlow to see sense.

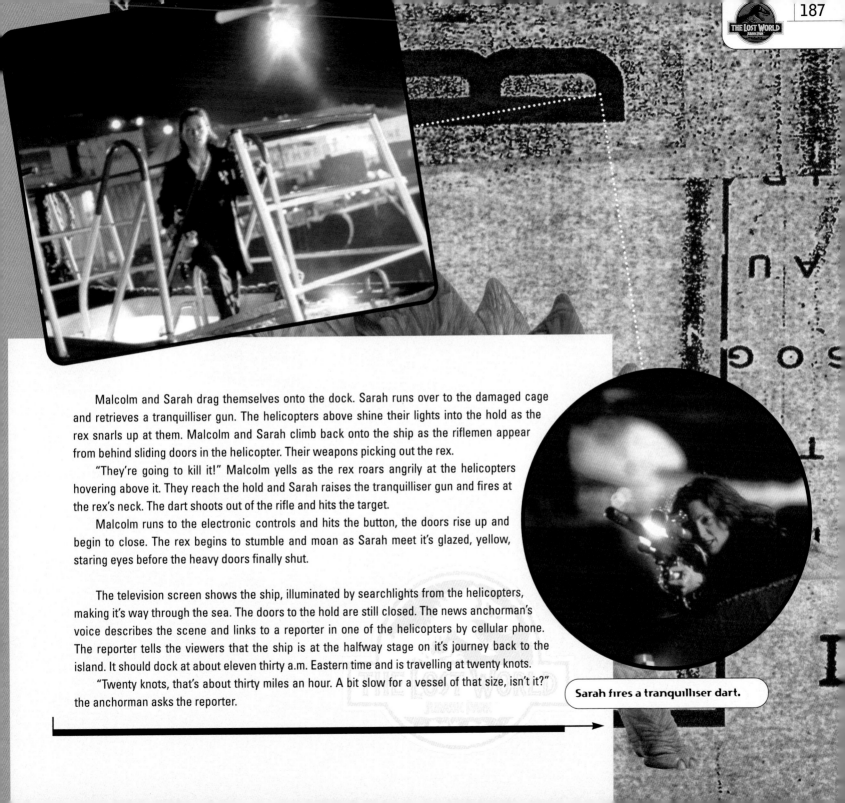

Malcolm and Sarah drag themselves onto the dock. Sarah runs over to the damaged cage and retrieves a tranquilliser gun. The helicopters above shine their lights into the hold as the rex snarls up at them. Malcolm and Sarah climb back onto the ship as the riflemen appear from behind sliding doors in the helicopter. Their weapons picking out the rex.

"They're going to kill it!" Malcolm yells as the rex roars angrily at the helicopters hovering above it. They reach the hold and Sarah raises the tranquilliser gun and fires at the rex's neck. The dart shoots out of the rifle and hits the target.

Malcolm runs to the electronic controls and hits the button, the doors rise up and begin to close. The rex begins to stumble and moan as Sarah meet it's glazed, yellow, staring eyes before the heavy doors finally shut.

The television screen shows the ship, illuminated by searchlights from the helicopters, making it's way through the sea. The doors to the hold are still closed. The news anchorman's voice describes the scene and links to a reporter in one of the helicopters by cellular phone. The reporter tells the viewers that the ship is at the halfway stage on it's journey back to the island. It should dock at about eleven thirty a.m. Eastern time and is travelling at twenty knots.

"Twenty knots, that's about thirty miles an hour. A bit slow for a vessel of that size, isn't it?" the anchorman asks the reporter.

Sarah fires a tranquilliser dart.

THE LOST WORLD
JURASSIC PARK

The baby T-rex
gets its revenge.

The horror is finally over.

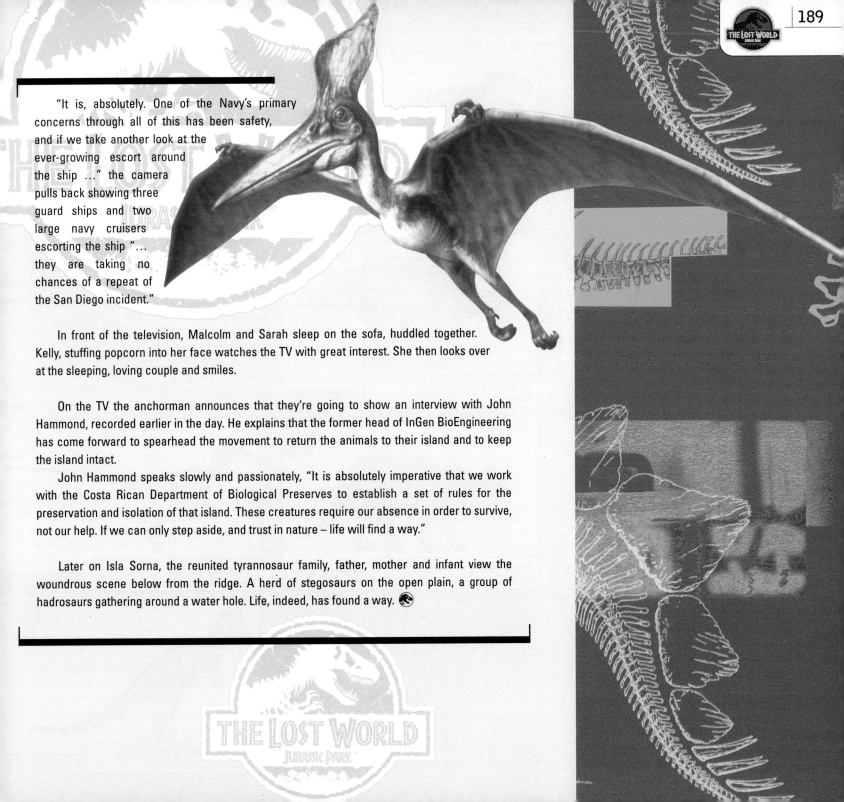

"It is, absolutely. One of the Navy's primary concerns through all of this has been safety, and if we take another look at the ever-growing escort around the ship …" the camera pulls back showing three guard ships and two large navy cruisers escorting the ship "… they are taking no chances of a repeat of the San Diego incident."

In front of the television, Malcolm and Sarah sleep on the sofa, huddled together. Kelly, stuffing popcorn into her face watches the TV with great interest. She then looks over at the sleeping, loving couple and smiles.

On the TV the anchorman announces that they're going to show an interview with John Hammond, recorded earlier in the day. He explains that the former head of InGen BioEngineering has come forward to spearhead the movement to return the animals to their island and to keep the island intact.

John Hammond speaks slowly and passionately, "It is absolutely imperative that we work with the Costa Rican Department of Biological Preserves to establish a set of rules for the preservation and isolation of that island. These creatures require our absence in order to survive, not our help. If we can only step aside, and trust in nature – life will find a way."

Later on Isla Sorna, the reunited tyrannosaur family, father, mother and infant view the woundrous scene below from the ridge. A herd of stegosaurs on the open plain, a group of hadrosaurs gathering around a water hole. Life, indeed, has found a way.

TYRANNOSAURUS REX
HEIGHT 13'-5" • LENGTH 33'-0"

BABY TYRANNOSAURUS REX
HEIGHT 3'-5⁵/₈" • LENGTH 6'-3³/₁₆"

STEGOSAURUS
HEIGHT 12'-4³/₄" • LENGTH 25'-2¹/₂"

BABY STEGOSAURUS
HEIGHT 4'-5¹/₈" • LENGTH 7'-11⁵/₈"

TRICERATOPS
HEIGHT 8'-10³/₄" • LENGTH 20'-9⁹/₁₆"

BABY TRICERATOPS
HEIGHT 3'-4" • LENGTH 6'-3"

VELOCIRAPTOR
HEIGHT 5'-5" • LENGTH 13'-2³/₄"

PACHYCEPHALOSAURUS
HEIGHT 4'-11¹/₈" • LENGTH 8'-1⁹/₁₆"

Dinosaur FACTS

COMPSOGNATHUS

Order of the Coelursaur. Very lizard like, they were one of the smallest known dinosaurs, known for eating their own species.

MAMENTIASAURUS

Order of the Saurischian, suborder of Sauropodomorphia, the name Mamentiasaurus is derived from the place it was first discovered, Mamechi. A planteating dinosaur with a neck span accounting for nearly half the body length, 15 vertebrae to be exact.

PACHYCEPHALOSAURUS

Order of the Ornithischian, suborder of Pachipaurus. Known for their thick bone of the upper skull used in social interactions, territory countership and defence. Plant eating, trunk headed reptile known for intelligence.

PARASAUROLOPHUS

Member of the Hadrosauridae family, order of the Ornithischian, resized reptile. Plant eating dinosaur known as a Bi-Pedal vegetarian. It is distinguished by its skull crest, an elongated curved structure longer than the entire skull. Weighing more than two tons, it was built to walk on all fours as well as on two legs.

PTERANODON

Largest of the Archosaurian flying reptiles. Many had fur-covered bodies and may have been warm blooded.

STEGOSAURUS

Suborder of armoured, Ornithischian dinosaurs which were abundant during the Jurassic Period. A plant eating dinosaur with a double row of boney plates along the spine, which contributed to their heavy, slow moving characteristics.

TRICERATOPS

Order of the Ornithischia, suborder of Ceratopsia. A large plant eating dinosaur known as the "three-horned face". The tri-top was one of the last surviving dinosaurs. Could move at very high speed, much like a rhinoceros.

TYRANNOSAURUS REX

Derived from "Tyrant" Reptile. Order of the Saurischian, Suborder of Theropoda. Among the largest and most powerful land carnivore dinosaurs. With a head 4.5ft long and 6in serrated teeth, they became the most feared dinosaurs.

VELOCIRAPTOR

Order of the Saurischian, suborder of Theropoda. The raptor was swift, smart, and equipped with sharp teeth, large eyes, and long clawed fingers and toes. Although no larger than a wolf, the raptor was known for its strength. The most distinguishing feature was a sickle-like claw on the second toe of its hind foot.

PTERANODON
WING SPAN 8'-$\frac{1}{2}$"

PARASAUROLOPHUS
HEIGHT 11'-4$\frac{1}{2}$" • LENGTH 16'-1"